Grade 1-2 Summer Activity Playground

12 weeks of Summer Activities:

- → Math
- → ELA
- → Science
- → Reading
- → Social Studies

Brain Hunter Prep is a division of ArgoPrep dedicated to providing high-quality workbooks for K-8th grade students. We have been awarded multiple awards for our curriculum, books and/or online program. Here are a few of our awards!

Our goal is to make your life easier, so let us know how we can help you by e-mailing us at: info@argoprep.com.

ISBN: 9781951048167
Published by Brain Hunter Prep.

Aknowlegments:
Icons made by Freepik, Creaticca Creative Agency, Pixel perfect , Pixel Buddha, Smashicons, Twitter , Good Ware, Smalllikeart, Nikita Golubev, monkik, DinosoftLabs, Icon Pond from www.flaticon.com

- ArgoPrep is a recipient of the prestigious **Mom's Choice Award**.
- ArgoPrep also received the 2019 **Seal of Approval** from Homeschool.com for our award-winning workbooks.
- ArgoPrep was awarded the 2019 **National Parenting Products Award, Gold Medal Parent's Choice Award** and a **Brain Child Award**

Want an amazing offer from ArgoPrep?

7 DAY ACCESS
to our online premium content at **www.argoprep.com**

Online premium content includes practice quizzes and drills with video explanations and an automatic grading system.

Chat with us live at

www.argoprep.com for this exclusive offer.

Summer Activity Playground Series

Kindergarten
Summer Activity Playground

12 weeks of Summer Activities:
- Math
- ELA
- Science
- Reading
- Social Studies

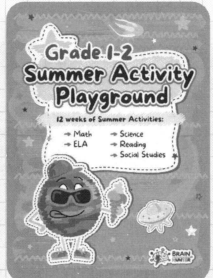

Grade 1-2
Summer Activity Playground

12 weeks of Summer Activities:
- Math
- ELA
- Science
- Reading
- Social Studies

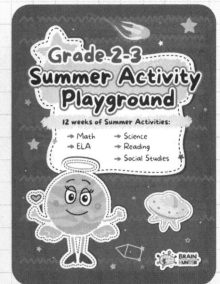

Grade 2-3
Summer Activity Playground

12 weeks of Summer Activities:
- Math
- ELA
- Science
- Reading
- Social Studies

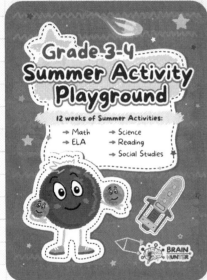

Grade 3-4
Summer Activity Playground

12 weeks of Summer Activities:
- Math
- ELA
- Science
- Reading
- Social Studies

Grade 4-5
Summer Activity Playground

12 weeks of Summer Activities:
- Math
- ELA
- Science
- Reading
- Social Studies

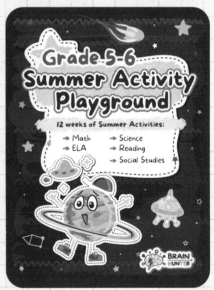

Grade 5-6
Summer Activity Playground

12 weeks of Summer Activities:
- Math
- ELA
- Science
- Reading
- Social Studies

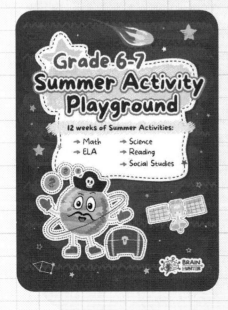

Grade 6-7
Summer Activity Playground

12 weeks of Summer Activities:
- Math
- ELA
- Science
- Reading
- Social Studies

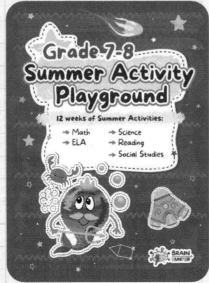

Grade 7-8
Summer Activity Playground

12 weeks of Summer Activities:
- Math
- ELA
- Science
- Reading
- Social Studies

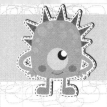

How to use this book?

Welcome to **Summer Activity Playground by Brain Hunter Prep!**

This workbook is specifically designed to prepare students over the summer to get ready for **Grade 2**. Our workbook is divided into twelve weeks so students can complete the entire workbook over the summer.

Our workbooks have been carefully designed and crafted by licensed teachers to give students an incredible learning experience. Students will be able to practice mathematics, english activities, science experiments, social studies, and fitness activities. Give your child the education they deserve!

Summer list to read

We strongly encourage students to read several books throughout the summer. Below you will find a recommended summer reading list that we have compiled for students entering into Grade 2. You can see this list at: www.argoprep.com/**summerlist**

Author: Lenore Look
Title: Alvin Ho

Author: Barbara Park
Title: Junie B. Jones

Author: Elise Broach
Title: The Miniature World of Marvin and James

Author: Jory John
Title: Giraffe Problems

Author: Cynthia Rylant
Title: Life

Author: Jason Chin
Title: Grand Canyon

Author: Bridget Heos
Title: I, Fly: The Buzz About Flies and How Awesome They Are

Author: Sally Warner
Title: Absolutely Alfie

Author: Mark Hoffman
Title: Fruit Bowl

Author: Nicola Davies
Title: King of the Sky

OTHER BOOKS BY ARGOPREP

Here are some other test prep workbooks by ArgoPrep you may be interested in. All of our workbooks come equipped with detailed video explanations to make your learning experience a breeze! Visit us at **www.argoprep.com**

COMMON CORE MATH SERIES

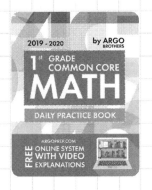 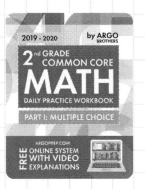  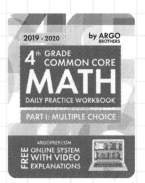

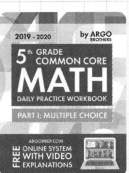 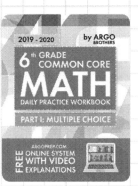 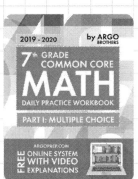 

COMMON CORE ELA SERIES

 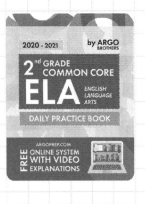  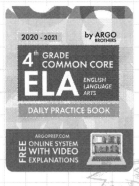

   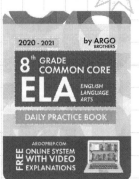

INTRODUCING MATH!

Introducing Math! by ArgoPrep is an award-winning series created by certified teachers to provide students with high-quality practice problems. Our workbooks include topic overviews with instruction, practice questions, answer explanations along with digital access to video explanations. Practice in confidence - with ArgoPrep!

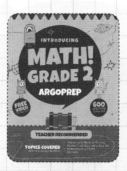
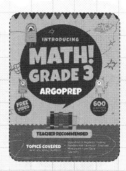

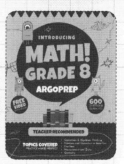
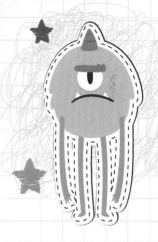

YOGA MINDFULNESS FOR KIDS

HIGHER LEVEL EXAMS

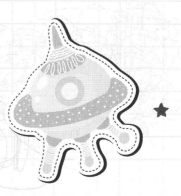

WORKBOOKS INCLUDED

Comprehensive K-8
Math & ELA Program

www.argoprep.com/k8

Math & ELA success begins here

Real Results, Close Learning Gaps, Boost Confidence

30,000+
Practice Questions

500+
Video Lectures

15,000+
of Video Explanations

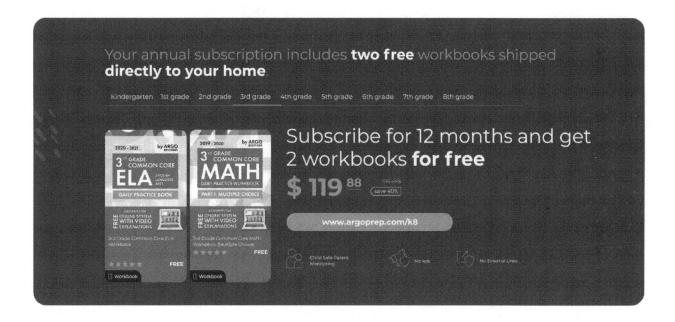
Printable

Worksheets, Games and more

Common Core

Next Generation Learning Standards & State Aligned

Grade 1-2
WEEK 1

Let's learn about:

* properties of operation
* irregular plural nouns
* classifying materials
* exploring your community and more!

1. What is the related fact for $3 + 4 = 7$?

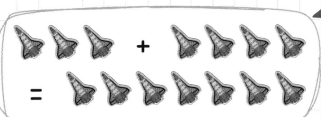

A. $4 + 3 = 7$ C. $1 + 6 = 7$

B. $3 + 7 = 10$ D. $4 + 4 = 8$

2. What is the related fact for $1 + 8 = 9$?

A. $8 + 1 = 9$ C. $8 - 1 = 7$

B. $9 + 1 = 10$ D. $1 + 1 = 8$

3. What is the related fact for $2 + 8 = 10$?

A. $8 - 2 = 6$ C. $2 + 2 = 8$

B. $8 + 2 = 10$ D. $4 + 4 = 8$

4. What is the related fact for $4 + 5 = 9$?

A. $4 + 4 = 8$ C. $5 + 4 = 9$

B. $5 + 5 = 10$ D. $9 + 4 = 13$

5. What is the related fact for $5 + 3 = 8$?

A. $8 + 3 = 11$ C. $8 + 5 = 12$

B. $3 + 5 = 8$ D. $11 + 3 = 14$

6. What is the related fact for $2 + 4 = 6$?

A. $2 + 2 = 4$ C. $4 + 2 = 6$

B. $4 + 4 = 8$ D. $6 + 6 = 12$

1. What is the related fact for 6 - 1 = 5?

A. 5 - 5 = 0   C. 6 - 5 = 1

B. 6 - 4 = 2   D. 5 - 6 = 1

2. What is the related fact for 10 - 7 = 3?

A. 10 - 5 = 5   C. 10 - 2 = 7

B. 10 - 3 = 7   D. 10 - 6 = 4

3. What is the related fact for 8 - 6 = 2?

A. 8 - 2 = 6   C. 8 - 4 = 4

B. 8 + 2 = 10   D. 8 - 1 = 6

4. What is the related fact for 4 - 1 = 3?

A. 4 - 2 = 2   C. 4 - 3 = 1

B. 4 - 1 = 2   D. 4 - 4 = 0

5. What is the related fact for 7 - 3 = 4?

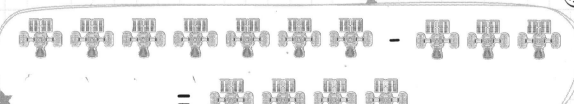

A. 7 - 4 = 3   B. 7 - 5 = 2   C. 7 - 2 = 5   D. 7 - 1 = 6

13

* A **noun** is a person, place or thing.
  * **Examples:** boy, school, book, bush

* **A plural noun** means there is more than one person, place or thing. To make a noun plural, we usually add -s or -es to the end of the word.
  * **Examples:** boys, schools, books, bushes

* An **irregular plural noun** means more than one person, place or thing but does not follow the -s and -es rule.
  * **Examples:** tooth → teeth, mouse → mice

It is important to use the correct form of irregular plural nouns when speaking and writing. You will now practice this below.

Directions: Write the correct irregular plural noun for each singular noun listed below.

1. Foot ..... Feet ....

2. Fish ..... Fishes ....

3. Deer ..... Deers ....

4. Goose ....

5. Leaf ....

6. Child ....

7. Man ....

8. Person ....

Week 1   Phonics Review

Topic 2   Long and Short Vowels

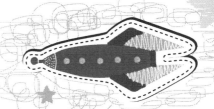

* A **short vowel** says the sound the letter can make that is not its name.
  * **Examples:** cat, bed, rip, hop, mud

* A **long vowel** says its name.
  * **Examples:** lake, teeth, ride, rope, mute

Directions: Read each word. Decide if the vowel is short or long. Write short vowel or long vowel on the line.

1. Made ....

2. Sun ....

3. Rob ....

4. Hope ....

5. Head ....

Directions: Complete the table below by writing short and long vowel words and placing them in the correct column.

Short Vowel Words	Long Vowel Words

FITNESS PLANET ➡ Let's get some fitness in! Go to page 167 to try some fitness activities.

15

Just about any material can be classified by its observable properties.
Observable properties are the characteristics of different materials that
you can observe with your senses such as: color, texture, flexibility, weight, size,
shape and hardness.

Today you are going to conduct an experiment to observe
and classify materials based on their properties.

Materials Needed:

* A variety of materials such as dry beans or pasta, paper, clothing, stuffed animal, coin, ball, plastic utensils, etc.

Procedure:

1. Collect 4-5 different materials that you want to observe.

2. Observe them using your five senses, according to the properties listed below.

3. Answer the follow-up questions.

Material	Color	Size	Shape	Weight

Follow-Up Questions:

1. Which materials could be classified as large?

....

....

2. Which materials could be classified as small?

....

....

3. Which materials could be classified as heavy?

....

....

4. Which materials could be classified as light?

....

....

5. Which materials are most alike?

....

....

1. $\boxed{7} + 5 = 12$

? + 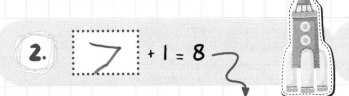 = 12

4. $\boxed{2} + 6 = 8$

? + = 8

2. $\boxed{7} + 1 = 8$

? + = 8

5. $\boxed{7} + 3 = 10$

? + = 10

3. $\boxed{5} + 2 = 7$

? + = 7

6. $\boxed{5} + 4 = 9$

? + = 9

18

1. If $6 + 1 = 7$, then $7 - 1 =$ **6**

$$\begin{array}{r} 7 \\ -\ 1 \\ \hline \end{array}$$

4. If $2 + 8 = 10$, then $10 - 8 =$ **2**

$$\begin{array}{r} 10 \\ -\ 8 \\ \hline \end{array}$$

2. If $4 + 2 = 6$, then $6 - 2 =$ **4**

$$\begin{array}{r} 6 \\ -\ 2 \\ \hline \end{array}$$

5. If $5 + 3 = 8$, then $8 - 5 =$ **3**

$$\begin{array}{r} 8 \\ -\ 5 \\ \hline \end{array}$$

3. If $7 + 5 = 12$, then $12 - 5 =$ **7**

$$\begin{array}{r} 12 \\ -\ 5 \\ \hline \end{array}$$

6. If $3 + 6 = 9$, then $9 - 6 =$ **3**

$$\begin{array}{r} 9 \\ -\ 6 \\ \hline \end{array}$$

FITNESS PLANET → Let's get some fitness in! Go to page 167 to try some fitness activities.

Read the passage below. Then answer the questions that follow.

One cold and windy day in January, Sam was walking to school with his sister and brother. They were complaining about being cold, and he was getting tired of listening to them.

"I'm going to run up ahead," Sam called out to them. "I'll see you when you get there."

Sam knew he wasn't supposed to let them walk by themselves, but he didn't want to listen to them anymore. He took off running, leaving them behind. He could see the school up ahead. What could possibly happen?

When he arrived at school, he went to the cafeteria for breakfast. He decided he would wait for his brother and sister to arrive before going to join his friends in the hallway.

A few minutes later, they walked into the cafeteria, covered in snow and shivering.

"What happened to you?" Sam asked. His sister looked very mad.

"What happened? A snowplow drove by and snow was flying everywhere. It looked like it was raining snow. We were covered in it. I brushed it off of Charlie as best as I could," his sister replied angrily.

Charlie was standing next to her, looking like he was trying not to cry. They both looked very wet.

"I'm sorry," Sam told them. "I should not have left you. Let's go call mom and see if she can bring you dry clothes."

As they walked to the school office, he knew he had made a mistake and that his mom was going to be very upset with him.

What a way to start off the day, he thought glumly. He wasn't going to make that mistake again!

Now answer the following questions about the reading passage.

1. Who is the main character in the passage?

....

2. Who are the supporting characters in the passage?

....

3. Where does the passage take place?

....

4. When does the passage take place? What clues help you to know this?

....

5. Why does Sam leave his brother and sister behind as they're walking to school?

....

6. What happens to Sam's brother and sister as they are walking to school?

....

7. Why is Sam's sister angry when she arrives at school?

....

8. How does Sam feel after seeing how angry his sister is? How do you know this from clues in the text?

....

9. How do you think Sam's mom is going to react when she finds out Sam left his brother and sister alone while walking to school?

....

10. What happens when you break a rule at home or at school?

....

....

....

Example:

$5 + 3 = 8$

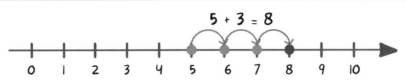

1. Use a number line to add 1 to **2**.

2. Use a number line to add 4 to **6**.

3. Use a number line to add 2 to **5**.

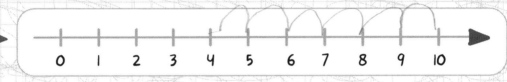

4. Use a number line to add 5 to 1.

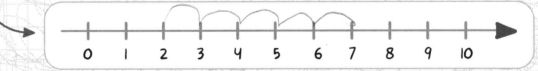

5. Use a number line to add 3 to **3**.

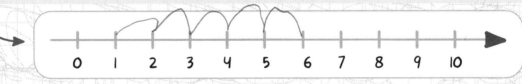

6. Use a number line to add 6 to **4**.

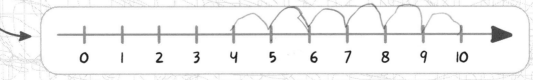

Today, you are going to explore your local community (city, town or village) by identifying when it was established, who the earliest settlers were and important people who have impacted the community. Use books, individuals and the internet to find the following information.

Name of Your Community: ....

Year the Community was Established: ....

Community Founded by: ....

Earliest Settlers: ....

What are 2 changes that have occurred over time in your community?

1. ....

   ....

2. ....

   ....

Name one person who has had a positive impact on your community.

....

....

....

On the lines below, describe the impact this person has had on the local community.

....

....

....

....

FITNESS PLANET ➡ Let's get some fitness in! Go to page 167 to try some fitness activities.

FITNESS

Grade 1-2
WEEK 2

Get ready to explore:

* adding and subtracting to 20
* past tense verbs
* vowel teams
* liquids and solids
* informational texts and more!

BRAIN HUNTER

1. 1 + 5 = 6

1 +

2. 6 + 5 = 11

3. 9 + 0 = 9

+ 9

4. 2 + 9 = 11

5. 4 + 4 = 8

6. 3 + 1 = 4

1. $8 - 2 = \boxed{6}$

$$\begin{array}{r} 8 \\ -\ 2 \\ \hline \end{array}$$

2. $3 - 1 = \boxed{2}$

$$\begin{array}{r} 3 \\ -\ 1 \\ \hline \end{array}$$

3. $9 - 8 = \boxed{1}$

$$\begin{array}{r} 9 \\ -\ 8 \\ \hline \end{array}$$

4. $5 - 2 = \boxed{3}$

$$\begin{array}{r} 5 \\ -\ 2 \\ \hline \end{array}$$

5. $4 - 4 = \boxed{0}$

$$\begin{array}{r} 4 \\ -\ 4 \\ \hline \end{array}$$

6. $10 - 5 = \boxed{5}$

$$\begin{array}{r} 10 \\ -\ 5 \\ \hline \end{array}$$

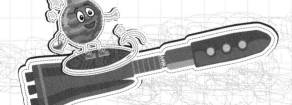

A **verb** is an action word. Verbs can be past tense (it already happened), present tense (it's happening right now) or future tense (it will happen in the future). We usually add -ed to the end of a verb to make it past tense.

  * **Examples:** walked, yelled, learned, cooked, jogged

An **irregular past tense verb** is one that does not follow the rule. Instead of adding -ed to the end of the verb, the word changes to become past tense.

  * **Examples:** ate, drank, shook, wrote, ran

Directions: Read the sentences below. Rewrite each sentence, changing the underlined verb from present tense to past tense.

1. I <u>ride</u> my bike to school.

   I rode my bike to school

2. My mom <u>pays</u> the cashier at the grocery store.

   My mom paid the cashier at the grocery store

3. Oliver <u>leaves</u> the room quietly.

   Oliver left the room quietly.

4. I <u>think</u> about going to the beach.

   I thought about going to the beach.

5. Gabby <u>builds</u> a castle with blocks.

   Gabby built a castle with block.

Directions: Now write your own sentences. First, write a sentence using a present tense irregular verb. Then, rewrite the sentence, changing the verb to past tense.

Present tense: *Grace is reading.*

Past tense: *Grace was reading.*

FITNESS PLANET → Let's get some fitness in! Go to page 167 to try some fitness activities.

Vowel teams are vowel sounds spelled with two vowels. The first vowel is long (it says its name) and the second vowel is silent.

* **Examples:** p<u>ai</u>d, t<u>ea</u>m, p<u>ie</u>, l<u>oa</u>d, d<u>ay</u>

Another way to remember how to sound out words with vowel teams is:

* **When 2 vowels go walking, the first one does the talking.**

* In other words, you always sound out the first vowel in the vowel team.

Directions: Below is a chart with some of the most common vowel teams. Complete the chart by thinking of words that have a vowel team in them.

ai	ay	ea
pail	day	beat
paii	stay	grit
paill	stay	each
paii	day	heart

ee	oe	ue
feet	toe	blue
beet	goet	rescue
meet	goe	cue
greet	hoe	due

ie	ow	oa
pie	blow	boat
variety	how	goat
die	plow	coat
	snow	float

28

Topic 1   Mixing Solids and Liquids

Solids and liquids can be mixed together with different results. Today, you are going to experiment with mixing a variety of solids and liquids together, predicting what the result will be and observing the properties of the mixture.

Materials Needed:

* A variety of solids (baking soda, flour, rice, sand, baking powder, etc.)
* A variety of liquids (water, vinegar, soda, etc.)
* Small cups
* A spoon or coffee stirrer

Procedure:

1. Set out the cups on a table or countertop.

2. Decide which solid and liquid will be mixed together. Write your prediction of the result on the chart below.

3. Mix the solid and liquid in the cup and stir.

4. Record your observations on the chart below.

	Solid	Liquid	Prediction	Observations
Experiment I				
Experiment 2				
Experiment 3				
Experiment 4				

Follow-Up Questions:

1. Did any of the mixtures result in a substance with different properties than the original materials?

....

....

....

....

....

....

....

....

....

....

....

1. $8 - 7 = \boxed{1}$

$$\begin{array}{r} 8 \\ -7 \\ \hline \end{array}$$

2. $7 + 3 = \boxed{10}$

$$\begin{array}{r} 7 \\ +3 \\ \hline \end{array}$$

3. $1 + 7 = \boxed{8}$

$1 +$

4. $10 - 3 = \boxed{7}$

$10 -$

5. $5 + 2 = \boxed{7}$

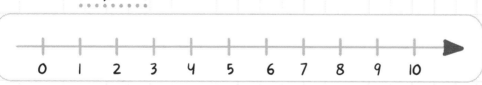

0 1 2 3 4 5 6 7 8 9 10

6. $4 - 1 = \boxed{}$

 FITNESS PLANET → Let's get some fitness in! Go to page 167 to try some fitness activities.

1. $6 + 4 =$ 10

$$\begin{array}{r} 6 \\ + 4 \\ \hline \end{array}$$

2. $8 - 4 =$ 4

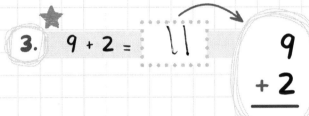

3. $9 + 2 =$ 11

$$\begin{array}{r} 9 \\ + 2 \\ \hline \end{array}$$

4. $6 + 6 =$ 12

$$\begin{array}{r} 6 \\ + 6 \\ \hline \end{array}$$

5. $7 - 5 =$ 2

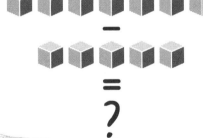

6. $2 + 1 =$ 3

$$\begin{array}{r} 2 \\ + 1 \\ \hline \end{array}$$

Read the passage below. Then answer the questions that follow.

Red-eared sliders are a type of medium-sized turtle commonly found in the United States. These turtles get their name from the red line found on their ears. Their shells are usually dark green to brownish-green in color, and the colors get darker as the turtle gets older.

Red-eared sliders are semi-aquatic, meaning they live in water but like to climb onto the land to warm up in the sun. They eat plants and smaller animals such as crickets, snails and worms.

Red-eared sliders have many predators, including raccoons, otters and foxes. When they sense danger is near, they slide into the water or pull their head and legs inside their shell. This keeps them safe from larger animals.

Turtles are reptiles, and reptiles do not hibernate in the winter. Red-eared sliders do become less active when the weather gets cold. During the winter, they live at the bottom of lakes and ponds.

Many people have turtles as pets. Do you think you would like a red-eared slider as your pet?

Answer the following questions about the reading passage.

1. What is the main topic of the passage?

Red-eared sliders

2. Is the purpose of the passage:
    A. to inform the reader
    B. to entertain the reader
    C. to persuade the reader

3. When do red-eared sliders become less active?

yes

4. What happens to red-eared sliders as they get older?

These shell get darker.

33

5. What is the author of the passage trying to describe to readers?

....

....

6. What do you think the word *hibernate* means in the passage?

....

....

7. Write 3 facts about red-eared sliders from the passage.

A. ....

B. ....

C. ....

8. Write your opinion of red-eared sliders on the lines below. Would you like a turtle for a pet?

....

....

$= 5$

$9 - 4$

3. How do you make 8?

....

....

A. 10 - 1   C. 10 - 2

B. 10 - 3   D. 10 - 4

1. How do you make 10?

....

....

A. 4 + 6   C. 5 + 6

B. 3 + 6   D. 6 + 6

4. How do you make 9?

....

....

A. 5 + 5   C. 5 + 4

B. 4 + 4   D. 4 + 6

2. How do you make 7?

....

....

A. 4 + 4   C. 6 + 2

B. 3 + 4   D. 8 + 1

5. How do you make 12?

....

....

A. 4 + 4   C. 6 + 6

B. 5 + 5   D. 7 + 7

 FITNESS
PLANET → Let's get some fitness in! Go to page
167 to try some fitness activities.

35

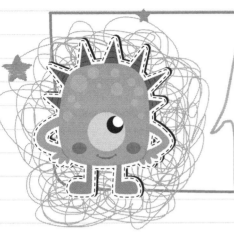

Today, you are going to take a closer look at a community celebration that takes place in your local community. This might be an annual festival, parade or other celebration. Research the community celebration by looking on the internet, in books or talking to community members. Then, answer the questions below.

Name of Your Local Community: ....

Name of Community Celebration: ....

Where and when does this celebration take place? ....

Who participates in this celebration? ....

What happens during the celebration?

....

....

....

What is the purpose of the celebration?

....

....

....

Why is this celebration important to the local community?

....

....

....

....

Grade 1-2
WEEK 3

It's time to master:

* equations
* prefixes
* heating and cooling materials
* opinion writing
* calendars and more!

Week 3 Operations and Algebraic Thinking

Topic 1 Addition and Subtract Equations

1. Which number sentence is **true**?

A. 2 + 5 = 6   C. 7 + 2 = 8

B. 5 + 1 = 6   D. 4 + 3 = 6

4. Which number sentence is **true**?

A. 2 + 7 = 10   C. 4 + 5 = 7

B. 3 + 2 = 5   D. 9 + 0 = 90

2. Which number sentence is **true**?

A. 1 + 4 = 5   C. 6 + 2 = 7

B. 3 + 6 = 8   D. 8 + 1 = 10

5. Which number sentence is **true**?

A. 10 - 3 = 13   C. 4 - 2 = 1

B. 7 - 6 = 3   D. 8 - 7 = 1

3. Which number sentence is **true**?

A. 1 + 3 = 6   C. 8 + 1 = 9

B. 5 + 4 = 8   D. 5 + 2 = 6

1. Which number sentence is **false?**

....

....

   A. 1 + 8 = 9   C. 7 + 3 = 11

   B. 5 + 4 = 9   D. 9 + 2 = 11

2. Which number sentence is **false?**

....

....

   A. 2 + 7 = 9   C. 6 + 3 = 9

   B. 4 + 1 = 3   D. 3 + 5 = 8

3. Which number sentence is **false?**

....

....

   A. 8 - 6 = 2   C. 4 - 2 = 2

   B. 6 - 2 = 2   D. 2 - 1 = 2

4. Which number sentence is **false?**

....

....

   A. 9 - 4 = 5   C. 5 - 3 = 2

   B. 7 - 5 = 4   D. 3 - 2 = 1

5. Which number sentence is **false?**

....

....

   A. 1 + 2 = 3   C. 5 - 2 = 7

   B. 3 + 2 = 5   D. 9 - 7 = 2

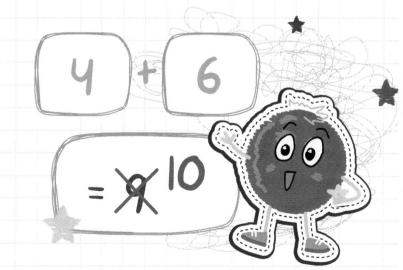

4 + 6

= ̶9̶ 10

FITNESS PLANET → Let's get some fitness in! Go to page 167 to try some fitness activities.

Verb tense is used to help the reader or listener know when the action is happening. There are **3** different verb tenses:

1. Past tense - the action already happened.

2. Present tense - the action is happening right now.

3. Future tense - the action will happen sometime in the future.

Past Tense	Present Tense	Future Tense
I <u>walked</u> to the store.	I <u>am walking</u> to the store.	I <u>will walk</u> to the store.

Directions: Complete the chart below with the correct past, present or future tense verb form.

Past Tense	Present Tense	Future Tense
shouted		
		will finish
	cooking	
		will play
climbed		

Directions: Choose any two words from the chart to write into complete sentences.

1. ....

   ....

2. ....

   ....

40

A prefix is a group of letters attached to the beginning of a word to change its meaning.

Prefix	Meaning	Example
pre-	before	preview
un-	not	undo
re-	again	replay

Directions: Read the prefix and base words below. Put them together and write the new word on the line.

1. pre + school = ...

2. un + tied = ...

3. re + write = ...

4. What is the meaning of the word in #1 when the prefix is added?
. . . .

5. What is the meaning of the word in #2 when the prefix is added?
. . . .

6. What is the meaning of the word in #3 when the prefix is added?
. . . .

7. Choose a prefix from the list above. Think of **3** other words that have that prefix. Write them below.

. . . .

. . . .

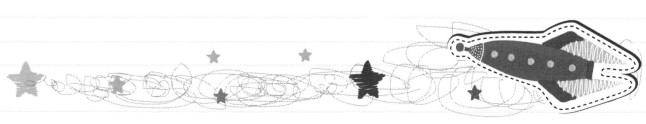

For most materials, heating or cooling the material will cause changes. Sometimes these changes can be reversed and sometimes they cannot. Today, you will experiment with reversing changes caused by heating and cooling.

Materials Needed:

* Water
* Cups
* Microwave
* Freezer

Procedure:

1. Fill a small cup with water and place in the freezer for **2** hours.

2. Record your observations below.

....
....
....

3. After **2** hours, remove the cup from the freezer and place in the microwave for 1 minute.

4. Record your observations below.

....
....
....

Week 3 Science

Topic 1 Changes Caused by Heating and Cooling

Follow-Up Questions:

1. What happened to the water after being in the freezer for 2 hours?

....

....

2. What happened after the cup was microwaved for 1 minute?

....

....

3. What can you conclude about heating and cooling water? Are the changes reversible?

....

....

4. Think of a material that, once heated or cooled, would not be able to change back to its original state.

....

....

5. Why are the changes to this material not reversible?

....

....

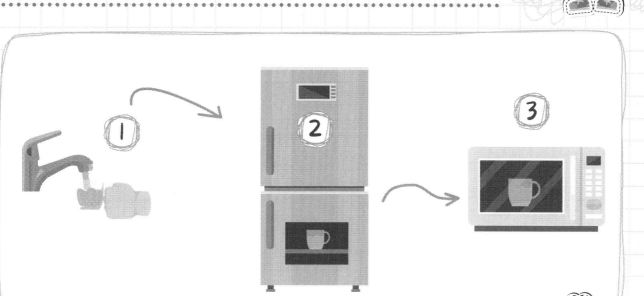

FITNESS PLANET ➡ Let's get some fitness in! Go to page 167 to try some fitness activities.

1. Which number can you add to 1 to get 5?

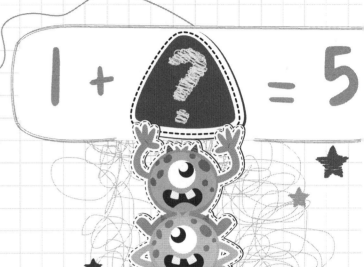

$$1 + \boxed{?} = 5$$

....

....

2. Which number can you add to 6 to get 8?

....

....

5. Which number can you add to 3 to get 4?

....

....

3. Which number can you add to 2 to get 6?

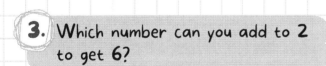

$$2 + \boxed{?} = 6$$

....

....

6. Which number can you add to 4 to get 7?

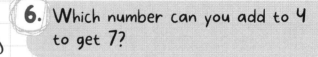

....

....

4. Which number can you add to 5 to get 9?

....

....

Week 3 Operations and Algebraic Thinking

Topic 2 Addition and Subtract Equations

1. Which number can you add to 6 to get 10?

....

....

2. Which number can you add to 2 to get 9?

....

....

3. Which number can you add to 1 to get 2?

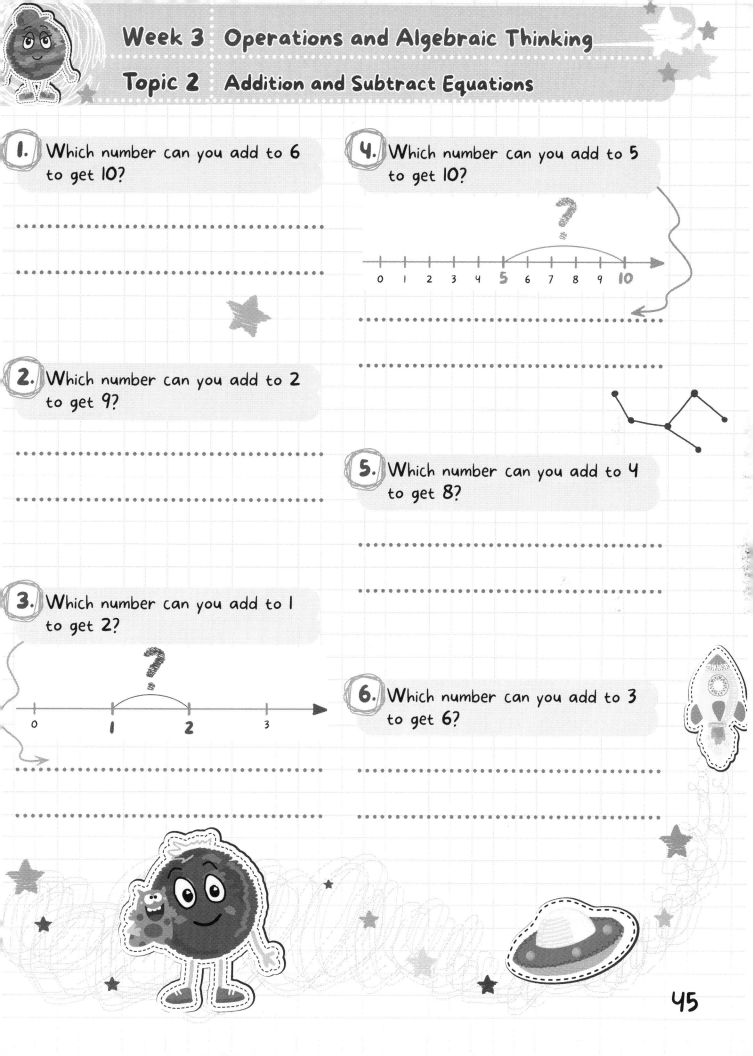

0   1   2   3

....

....

4. Which number can you add to 5 to get 10?

0 1 2 3 4 5 6 7 8 9 10

....

....

5. Which number can you add to 4 to get 8?

....

....

6. Which number can you add to 3 to get 6?

....

....

45

Opinion writing is when you state your opinion about a topic in an organized way and provide reasons to support your opinion.

Today you will practice writing a short opinion piece. In the paragraph, you will need to tell your opinion, give reasons to support your opinion and include a concluding statement. You will begin by thinking through each part that should be included in the paragraph.

Think about your favorite book. This book will be your topic for this writing piece. A **topic** is what you are writing about. You will always start any type of writing with a topic and often you will use it to introduce or begin your piece of writing.

Topic: ....

Your opinion should reflect that this is your favorite book. You should always include your opinion right at the beginning of any piece of opinion writing.

Opinion: ....

....

....

Think of at least **3** reasons why this is your favorite book. You will use these as supporting details in your writing. You should develop each reason to a sentence or two in your writing piece.

Reason #1: ....

....

....

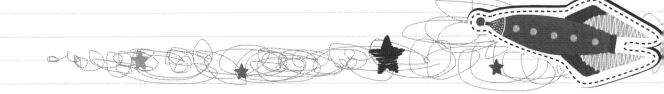

Reason #2: ....

....

....

Reason #3: ....

....

....

A **concluding statement** is a way to wrap up your writing. It should sum up your opinion and give the reader an idea of whether or not you recommend something or what you think should be done next. Since you are writing about your favorite book, do you think the reader should read this book? **Why?**

....

....

....

....

Concluding statement:

Now you will use the graphic organizer you created above to write a well-organized opinion piece about your favorite book on the lines below. Be sure your writing includes an opinion statement, at least **3** reasons to support your opinion and a concluding statement. Remember to write in complete sentences and use capital letters and correct punctuation.

....

....

....

....

....

....

....

....

FITNESS PLANET ➡ Let's get some fitness in! Go to page 167 to try some fitness activities.

47

1. There are four frogs in a pond. Two more jump in. How many frogs are there now?

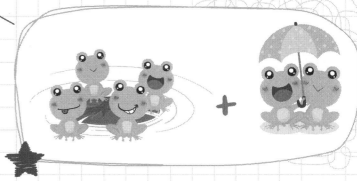

....

....

2. There are six frogs in a pond. Three jump out. How many frogs are there now?

....

....

3. There are ten fish in a pond. A boy catches three of them. How many fish are left?

....

....

4. There are three children in our family. We each bring a friend to the beach. How many children are going to the beach?

....

....

5. There are seven umbrellas on the beach. Two blow away in the wind. How many umbrellas are left?

....

....

6. There are eleven lifeguards assigned to a beach. Two leave to have their lunch. How many are left?

....

....

Calendars are important tools in helping people keep track of important days and stay organized.

Today, you are going to create a calendar of important days, holidays and events that are important to your life.

First, use the space below to brainstorm any days or events that should be included on your calendar.

School
· ·
· ·
· ·

Sports/Activities
· ·
· ·
· ·

Cultural/Religious
· ·
· ·
· ·

Family
· ·
· ·
· ·

Friends
· ·
· ·
· ·

Other
· ·
· ·
· ·

Now use the information from your brainstorm list to create a calendar. This calendar can be for one week, one month or even one year. Be sure to include dates and all the special or important events that are relevant to your life.

· ·
· ·
· ·
· ·

SEPTEMBER						
SU	MO	TU	WE	TH	FR	SA
		my birthday!	1		2	3
4	5	6	(7)	8	9	10
11	12	13	14	15	16	17
18	19	20	21	22	23	24
25	26	27	28	29	30	31

49

Grade 1-2
WEEK 4

Let's practice:

* adding **3** whole numbers
* using adjectives and adverbs
* exploring clouds
* reading comprehension and more!

1. 1 + 3 + 9

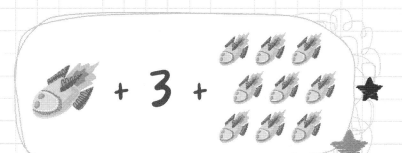

A. 12   B. 13   C. 14   D. 14

2. 5 + 9 + 3

A. 18   C. 16

B. 17   D. 15

3. 8 + 6 + 2

A. 16   C. 18

B. 17   D. 19

4. 5 + 4 + 8

A. 15   B. 16   C. 17   D. 18

5. 6 + 2 + 4

A. 15   C. 13

B. 14   D. 12

6. 2 + 5 + 7

A. 14   C. 16

B. 15   D. 17

FITNESS PLANET → Let's get some fitness in! Go to page 167 to try some fitness activities.

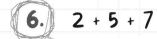

1. 4 + 8 + 2

A. 11   C. 13

B. 12   D. 14

2. 3 + 3 + 6

A. 10   C. 12

B. 11   D. 13

3. 7 + 1 + 4

A. 11   C. 13

B. 12   D. 14

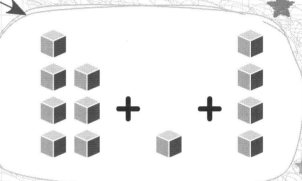

4. 1 + 4 + 5

A. 9   C. 11

B. 10   D. 12

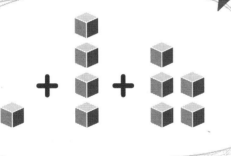

5. 5 + 2 + 1

A. 6   C. 8

B. 7   D. 9

6. 4 + 7 + 3

A. 12   C. 14

B. 13   D. 14

Week 4 Language Review

Topic 1 Adjectives and Adverbs

An **adjective** is a word that describes a noun.

* **Examples:** <u>fancy</u> dinner, <u>brave</u> child, <u>jealous</u> friend, <u>gigantic</u> dinosaur

An **adverb** is a word that describes an adjective or verb.

* **Examples:** <u>quietly</u> whispered, moved <u>away</u>, ran <u>yesterday</u>, <u>extremely</u> tired

Directions: Read the nouns below. On each line, write an adjective that could be used to describe each one.

1. Cat ....

2. Teacher ....

3. Museum ....

4. Pizza ....

5. Policeman ....

Directions: Read the verbs and adjectives below. On each line, write an adverb that could be used to describe each one.

1. Shout ....

2. Jog ....

3. Happy ....

4. Sang ....

5. Cooked ....

Directions: Read the sentences below. Fill in the blank with an adjective or adverb that makes sense. Then, identify the word as an adjective or an adverb by circling the correct option below the sentence.

1. He put the .... book down on the table beside him.

   Adjective   Adverb

2. The choir sang .... so that everyone could hear them.

   Adjective   Adverb

3. The girl's new teacher had a very .... face.

   Adjective   Adverb

4. My mom took our dog for a .... walk.

   Adjective   Adverb

5. We were .... tired after playing at the new playground.

   Adjective   Adverb

6. The little boy is talking ....

   Adjective   Adverb

7. The queen's .... dress was covered in jewels.

   Adjective   Adverb

There are three main types of clouds: cirrus, stratus and cumulus. Today you are going to observe the sky and sketch the types of clouds you see.

Cirrus clouds are white and feathery and are found very high in the sky.

Stratus clouds are wide blankets of clouds found lower in the sky.

Cumulus clouds are large and puffy with flat bottoms and are found low in the sky.

Materials Needed:

* Paper

* Drawing utensil

Procedure:

1. On a day with lots of clouds in the sky, go outside and observe the clouds.

2. Sketch the clouds you see below and answer the follow-up questions.

FITNESS PLANET → Let's get some fitness in! Go to page 167 to try some fitness activities.

Sketch your observations here:

Follow-Up Questions

1. What type or types of clouds did you observe in the sky?

   ....

   ....

2. Which characteristics helped you identify the types of clouds you observed?

   ....

   ....

1. $8 + 3 + 5$

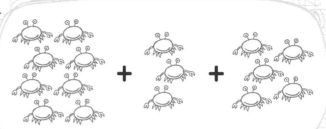

....

....

2. $5 + 6 + 5$

....

....

3. $3 + 1 + 3$

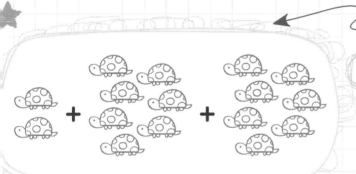

4. $2 + 7 + 7$

....

....

5. $1 + 5 + 4$

....

....

6. $9 + 4 + 6$

....

....

1. 4 + 8 + 3

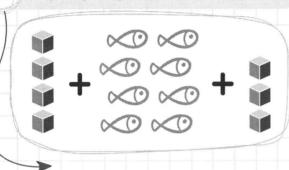

....

2. 7 + 7 + 8

....

3. 6 + 2 + 9

....

4. 1 + 9 + 1

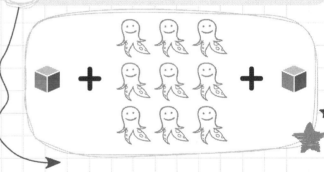

....

5. 9 + 4 + 2

....

6. 4 + 6 + 2

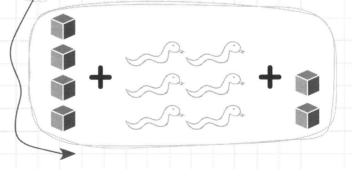

....

Read the following passage. Then, answer the questions that follow.

Today, Tina's grandmother was coming to visit her and her family. Grandmother lives in New York City which is very far away from Tina's home in Kansas. Tina and her brothers don't get to see their grandmother very often so it's special when she comes to visit. Grandmother loves to sing and dance and play games with them, she cooks delicious meals and she always brings them a small present from the city.

When Grandmother arrived, Tina and her brothers met her excitedly at the front door and gave her big hugs. After they helped her put her luggage away in the extra bedroom, Grandmother pulled out three small packages, one for Tina and each of her brothers. The three kids could hardly contain their excitement as they unwrapped the blue and red wrapping paper and opened the boxes.

Tina opened her box, wondering what could be inside. As she peeled back the layers of tissue paper, she saw a flat, white keychain with a picture of the New York skyline. Underneath the picture was her name in red letters. She loved it!

She could see that her brothers had gotten matching keychains as well. Tina ran over and threw her arms around her grandmother. She knew this week with her grandmother was going to be so special!

Now answer the following questions about the reading passage.

1. What happens at the beginning of the passage?

....

....

....

2. How do Tina and her brothers react when Grandmother arrives?

....

....

....

FITNESS PLANET ➡ Let's get some fitness in! Go to page 167 to try some fitness activities.

FITNESS

3. How did Tina feel about the gift Grandmother brought her? How did you know?

....

....

....

4. What is your opinion of the gift that grandmother brought Tina?

....

....

....

5. Why do Tina and her brothers rarely see their grandmother?

....

....

....

6. List 3 things Grandmother does when she visits.
   A. ....
   B. ....
   C. ....

7. How does the passage end?

....

....

....

8. If one of your family members came to visit you and brought a present, what would you want it to be and why?

....

....

....

1. My sister collects stickers. She gets **5** heart stickers, **3** bear stickers and **10** letter stickers. How many stickers is she adding to her collection?

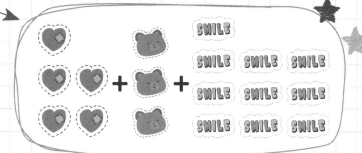

2. We had to plant flowers in our garden. We planted **4** daisies, **1** sunflower and **7** tulips. How many flowers did we plant in all?

3. My dog hides bones around our house. We found **4** bones under my bed, **6** bones under the couch and **7** bones in the closet. How many bones has he hidden in all?

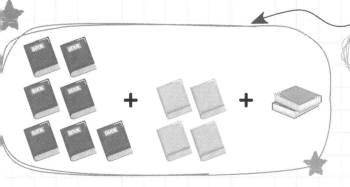

4. Our class spent the summer reading books. We read **7** sports books, **4** fiction books and **2** chapter books. How many books did we read in all?

5. Last week, we helped at our local pet shelter. We fed **5** cats, **9** dogs and **4** bunnies. How many animals does our pet shelter have in all?

6. We need to know how many rooms in our house need carpet. We have **4** bedrooms, **2** living rooms and an office. How many rooms need carpet?

The United States was founded on the belief of equal rights for all of its citizens.

Citizens are people with rights and responsibilities in a particular city, state, country or other community.

Rights are freedoms that citizens are entitled to as members of a particular community.

Responsibilities are the things that citizens are required to do as members of a particular community.

On the table below, brainstorm a list of rights and responsibilities that citizens of the United States have. An example has been provided.

Rights	Responsibilities
Freedom of speech	Treating other citizens with kindness and respect

Grade 1-2

WEEK 5

Let's get to work on:

* counting to 120
* simple/compound sentences
* making weather observations
* reading/writing numerals and more!

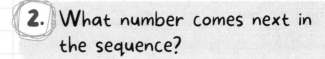

$$58 \rightarrow 59 \rightarrow 60 \rightarrow \text{?}$$

1. What number comes next in the sequence?

A. 58   C. 60

B. 59   D. _____

2. What number comes next in the sequence?

A. 111   C. 113

B. 112   D. _____

3. What number comes next in the sequence?

A. 23   C. 25

B. 24   D. _____

4. What number comes next in the sequence?

A. 107   C. 109

B. 108   D. _____

5. What number comes next in the sequence?

A. 69   C. 71

B. 70   D. _____

6. What number comes next in the sequence?

A. 45   C. 47

B. 46   D. _____

1. What number completes the sequence?

   A. 38   C. 40

   B. _____   D. 41

2. What number completes the sequence?

   A. 82   C. _____

   B. 83   D. 85

3. What number completes the sequence?

   A. _____   C. 98

   B. 97   D. 99

4. What number completes the sequence?

   A. 13   C. _____

   B. 14   D. 16

5. What number completes the sequence?

   A. _____   C. 116

   B. 115   D. 117

6. What number completes the sequence?

   A. 42   C. 44

   B. _____   D. 45

FITNESS PLANET → Let's get some fitness in! Go to page 167 to try some fitness activities.

A simple sentence is a complete thought that begins with a capital letter and ends with a punctuation mark.

* **Example:** The dog has black and white spots.

A compound sentence has two or more simple sentences joined together by and, or or but.

* **Example:** The dog has black and white spots, and his ears are long and floppy.

Directions: Write simple and compound sentences below.

1. Simple - ....

2. Simple - ....

3. Compound - ....

4. Compound - ....

Directions: Take each of the simple sentences written above and turn them into compound sentences.

1. ....

2. ....

Remember...
Long vowels say their name and **short vowels** say the other sound the letter makes.

Directions: Identify each word below as having a short vowel or long vowel.

1. Hop ....

2. Bump ....

3. Line ....

4. Fin ....

5. Gate ....

6. Bean ....

7. Mug ....

8. Mute ....

9. Nap ....

10. Load ....

Directions: Write 2 short vowel words and 2 long vowel words below.

1. Short - ....

2. Short - ....

3. Long - ....

4. Long - ....

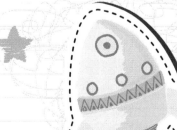

Today, you are going to observe the weather in your area and complete the chart below. Over a period of a few days, add to the chart. Then, answer the follow-up questions below.

Date	Temperature	Cloud Type(s)	Precipitation Type

FITNESS PLANET → Let's get some fitness in! Go to page 167 to try some fitness activities.

 FITNESS

Follow-Up Questions:

1. Write a summary of the weather that you observed.

....

....

....

....

2. Does the weather that you observed match the current season? Why or why not?

....

....

....

....

....

1. How many objects are there?

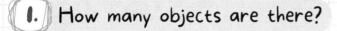

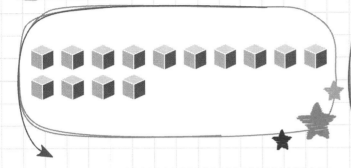

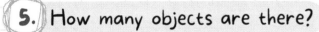

2. How many objects are there?

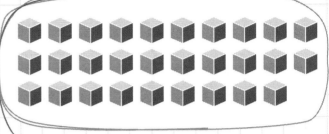

3. How many objects are there?

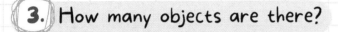

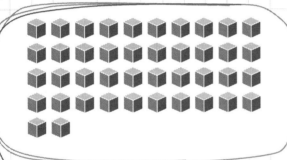

4. How many objects are there?

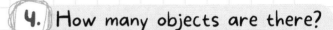

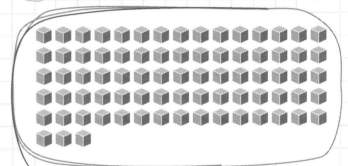

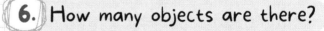

5. How many objects are there?

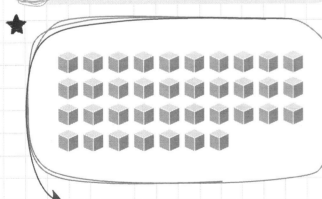

6. How many objects are there?

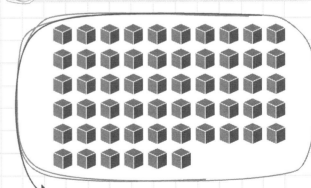

1. Circle **15** objects.

2. Circle **21** objects.

3. Circle **33** objects.

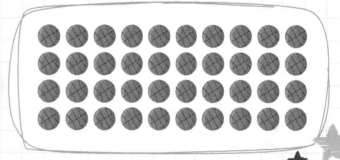

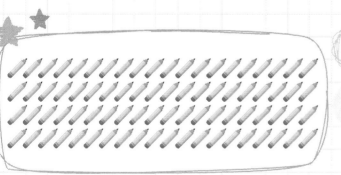

4. Circle **64** objects.

5. Circle **71** objects.

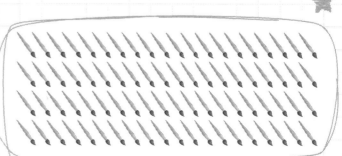

Informative writing is writing that teaches the reader about something (a topic).

Today you will practice writing a short informative piece. This organized paragraph on a specific topic will include an introduction of the topic, facts and other details that develop the topic and a concluding statement. You will begin by mapping out your writing and then put it together into a well-organized paragraph.

Think about a real thing that you know a lot about. Examples might include: a plant, an animal, a game, a sport, a geographic location or a subject area. This will be your topic for this writing piece. A **topic** is what you are writing about. You will always start any type of writing with a topic and often use it to introduce or begin your piece of writing.

Topic:

What is your topic? It should be used to introduce your writing in a well-developed sentence.

Supporting Details:

Think of at least **3** facts or details about your topic. You will use these as supporting details in your writing. You should develop each fact into a sentence or two in your writing piece.

Detail #1: ....

....

....

Detail #2: ....

....

....

Detail #3: ....

....

....

A **concluding statement** is a way to wrap up your writing. It should sum up your paragraph and give the reader an idea of how you feel about the topic.

···

···

···

···

Concluding statement:

Now you will use the graphic organizer you created above to write a well-organized informative piece about your topic on the lines below. Be sure your writing includes an introduction, at least **3** facts or details to develop your topic and a concluding statement. Remember to write in complete sentences and use capital letters and correct punctuation.

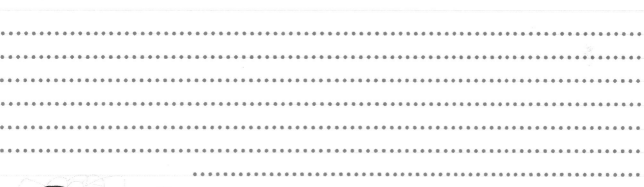

···

···

···

···

···

···

···

···

···

···

···

···

FITNESS PLANET ➡ Let's get some fitness in! Go to page 167 to try some fitness activities.

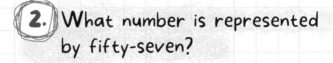

1. What number is represented by ninety-eight?

A. 98   C. 89

B. 99   D. 88

2. What number is represented by fifty-seven?

A. 75   C. 52

B. 57   D. 15

3. What number is represented by forty-one?

A. 14   C. 1

B. 4   D. 41

4. What number is represented by one hundred four?

A. 140   C. 104

B. 114   D. 41

5. What number is represented by one hundred twelve?

A. 111   C. 102

B. 121   D. 112

6. What number is represented by twenty-three?

A. 22   C. 23

B. 32   D. 33

Every community has a variety of leaders who are responsible for making and enforcing laws, and ensuring the rights of citizens.

Today, you are going to find out more about the leaders of your own local community. You may need to use the internet, books or ask community members for help.

The **mayor** is the elected head of a city or town.
Who is the mayor of your city or town? ....

The **city council** is a group of elected officials who work together to pass laws and supervise city government.
Who are the city council members in your city or town?

....

....

A **judge** is a public official appointed to decide cases in a court of law.
Who is the city or county judge in your community?

....

The **city clerk** is in charge of record keeping for the city.
Who is the city clerk in your city or town?

....

....

The **police chief** and **fire chief** are officials in command of the police and fire departments.
Who is the police chief in your city or town?

....

Who is the fire chief in your city or town?

....

Grade 1-2

WEEK 6

Get ready for a new adventure with:

* tens and ones
* erosion in action
* syllables
* good citizenship and more!

1. Circle 10 objects.

2. Circle 10 objects.

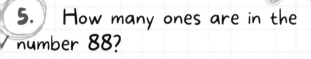

3. How many tens are in the number 42?

4. How many tens are in the number 21?

5. How many ones are in the number 88?

6. How many ones are in the number 69?

FITNESS PLANET → Let's get some fitness in! Go to page 167 to try some fitness activities.

FITNESS

77

1. How many ones are in the number 37?

....

....

2. How many tens are in the number 95?

....

....

3. How many tens are in the number 53?

....

....

4. How many ones are in the number 70?

....

....

5. How many tens are in the number 6?

....

....

6. How many ones are in the number 14?

....

....

When writing, it is important to remember that names of holidays and geographic locations should be capitalized. See the examples in the table below.

Holidays	Geographic Locations
Veteran's Day	California
Thanksgiving	New York City
Labor Day	Asia

Directions: Read each sentence below. Circle the word(s) that should be capitalized.

1. I can't wait for christmas morning!

2. This summer, their family will travel to germany, france and england.

3. Is mexico in north america or south america?

4. Do you prefer halloween or 4th of july?

5. She lived in tampa, florida before she moved to atlanta, georgia.

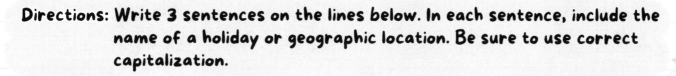

Directions: Write 3 sentences on the lines below. In each sentence, include the name of a holiday or geographic location. Be sure to use correct capitalization.

1. ....

2. ....

3. ....

Read the passage below. Then answer the questions that follow.

Making a peanut butter and jelly sandwich is simple! It only requires a few easy steps.

First, you need to gather all the ingredients and supplies. You will need peanut butter, jelly, bread, a knife and a plate. Second, you will place two slices of bread on the plate. Then, using the knife, spread peanut butter on one piece of bread and jelly on the other piece of bread. After that, you will press both pieces of bread together. Next, clean up all the ingredients. Lastly, enjoy eating your delicious peanut butter and jelly sandwich!

Directions: Answer the following questions about the reading passage.

1. What is the purpose of the passage?
   A. to entertain
   B. to explain
   C. to describe

2. What does the author want you to learn from this text? ....

3. What is the first step in making a peanut butter and jelly sandwich? ....

4. What should be done after spreading the peanut butter and jelly on each slice of bread?

5. What is the topic of this passage? ....

6. What is your opinion of peanut butter and jelly sandwiches? ....

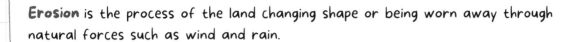

Erosion is the process of the land changing shape or being worn away through natural forces such as wind and rain.

Today, you are going to explore the process of erosion by performing two simple experiments that demonstrate the effects of wind and water erosion on landforms.

Materials Needed:

* Plastic storage container (small or medium-sized)
* Sand
* Pitcher of water

Procedure:

This experiment is best done outside, if possible.

1. Fill the storage container with sand.

2. Gently blow on the sand.

3. Record your observations below.

4. Now, pour the water slowly into the middle of the container of sand.

5. Record your observations below.

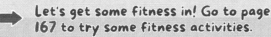

FITNESS PLANET → Let's get some fitness in! Go to page 167 to try some fitness activities.

Erosion Type	Observations
Wind Erosion	
Water Erosion	

Follow-Up Questions:

1. How might wind or water change the shape of land over time?

82

Week 6 Number and Operations in Base 10

Topic 2 Tens and Ones

1. 3 tens + 9 ones = ⭐

A. 93   C. 33

B. 39   D. 99

2. 1 tens + 8 ones = ⭐

A. 18   C. 88

B. 81   D. 15

3. 5 tens + 4 ones = ⭐

A. 55   C. 54

B. 44   D. 45

4. 6 tens + 3 ones = ⭐

A. 16   C. 63

B. 14   D. 36

5. 2 tens + 7 ones = ⭐

A. 27   C. 17

B. 72   D. 12

6. 4 tens + 0 ones = ⭐

A. 4   C. 14

B. 40   D. 41

1. Which number has 7 tens?

A. 17   C. 7

B. 79   D. 27

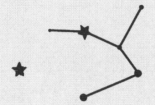

2. Which numbers has 6 ones?

A. 60   C. 68

B. 6   D. 33

3. Which numbers has 1 one?

A. 11   C. 12

B. 22   D. 86

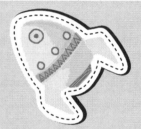

4. Which number has 8 tens?

A. 8   C. 38

B. 18   D. 80

5. Which numbers has 5 ones?

A. 45   C. 57

B. 24   D. 51

6. Which number has 0 tens?

A. 20   C. 17

B. 30   D. 4

Week 6 Phonics Review

Topic 3 Syllables

A **syllable** is the very basic part of words. Each syllable in a word includes a vowel sound and the surrounding consonants. See the table below for examples of words with different numbers of syllables.

1 syllable word	run
2 syllable word	hopping
3 syllable word	elephant
4 syllable word	ravioli

Directions: Read each word below. Count the syllables in the word. Circle the correct answer.

1. Butter
   - A. 1 syllable
   - B. 2 syllables
   - C. 3 syllables
   - D. 4 syllables

2. Fantastic
   - A. 1 syllable
   - B. 2 syllables
   - C. 3 syllables
   - D. 4 syllables

3. Sloth
   - A. 1 syllable
   - B. 2 syllables
   - C. 3 syllables
   - D. 4 syllables

4. Supermarket
   - A. 1 syllable
   - B. 2 syllables
   - C. 3 syllables
   - D. 4 syllables

5. Breakfast
   - A. 1 syllable
   - B. 2 syllables
   - C. 3 syllables
   - D. 4 syllables

6. Fly
   - A. 1 syllable
   - B. 2 syllables
   - C. 3 syllables
   - D. 4 syllables

FITNESS PLANET 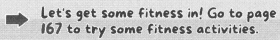 Let's get some fitness in! Go to page 167 to try some fitness activities.

Directions: On the lines below, write a word with the given number of syllables.

1. 1 syllable ....

....

2. 2 syllables ....

....

3. 3 syllables ....

....

4. 4 syllables ....

....

Directions: Practice reading the words below. These words all have more than one syllable and a long vowel.

1. Rainbow

....

2. Bathrobe

....

3. Flower

....

4. Open

....

5. Tiger

....

6. Teacher

....

Week 6   Number and Operations in Base 10

Topic 3   Sets of 10

1. How many tens are in this group?

....

2. How many tens are in this group?

....

3. How many tens are in this group?

....

4. How many tens are in this group?

....

5. How many tens are in this group?

....

6. How many tens are in this group?

....

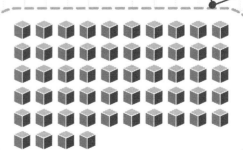

87

A **citizen** is someone with rights and responsibilities in a particular city, state, country or other community.

People who are good citizens typically have character traits that make them admirable.

Today, you are going to brainstorm the character traits that good citizens may have. Record your ideas on the chart below. An example has been provided.

Character Traits of Good Citizens

Respectful of all people, regardless of any differences

· ·

· ·

· ·

· ·

· ·

Follow-Up Questions

1. Who do you know that is a good citizen?

· ·

· ·

· ·

2. What makes them a good citizen?

· ·

· ·

· ·

FITNESS PLANET → Let's get some fitness in! Go to page 167 to try some fitness activities.

Grade 1-2
WEEK 7

It's time to explore:

* comparing two-digit numbers
* adding within 100
* commas in letters
* animal adaptations and more!

1. Which number is largest?

A. 42   C. 88

B. 24   D. 81

2. Which number is largest?

A. 17   C. 9

B. 71   D. 7

3. Which number is largest?

A. 31   C. 34

B. 32   D. 35

4. Which number is smallest?

A. 91   C. 9

B. 19   D. 21

5. Which number is smallest?

A. 16   C. 66

B. 61   D. 29

6. Which number is smallest?

A. 61   C. 78

B. 85   D. 92

Greater than (>), Less than (<), or Equal to (=)?

1. 15 ⬭ 42

2. 51 ⬭ 98

3. 70 ⬭ 26

4. 27 ⬭ 82

5. 33 ⬭ 49

6. 93 ⬭ 64

91

In a friendly letter, commas are found in both the greeting and closing of the letter. See the examples below.

Greeting: In the greeting of a letter, a comma is used at the end of the greeting, before the main body of the letter.

Dear Aunt Sue,

Closing: In the closing of a letter, a comma is used at the end of the closing, before the signature.

Sincerely,
Bobby

Directions: Read each greeting and closing below and write in the missing commas.

1. Dear Mr. Jones ....

2. Love Sue ....

3. Thank you Joe ....

4. Dear Mom ....

Directions: Read each greeting and closing below. Decide whether it is written correctly or not and circle the correct answer.

1. Dear Mr. President,

   A. Correct
   B. Incorrect

2. Thank, you Mrs. Black

   A. Correct
   B. Incorrect

 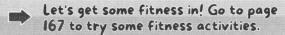

FITNESS PLANET ➡ Let's get some fitness in! Go to page 167 to try some fitness activities.

A friendly letter has **5** parts: the date, greeting, body, closing and signature. See below for more information about each of these parts.

Date: Write today's date at the top of the letter.

Greeting: Begin your letter with Dear and the name of the person you are writing to. Be sure to include a comma at the end of the greeting.

Body: This is the main text of your letter. You may ask questions or write statements in this part.

Closing: End your letter with a closing such as sincerely, thank you or love. Be sure to include a comma at the end of the closing.

Signature: Sign your name at the end so the reader knows who it is from.

Directions: Read the sample letter below. Then you will practice writing your own letter on the next page.

June 19, 2019

Dear Mom and Dad,

I am having so much fun at camp! Yesterday, I got to swim, hike through the forest, play games and sing songs. Plus, we roasted marshmallows at a campfire last night. I made a new friend. His name is John. He lives in Michigan. I love camp, but I miss you too.

Have you guys done anything fun without me? How are Gabby and Daniel? Tell them I said hi and give Lucky a big hug from me. See you Sunday!

Love,
Sam

On the lines below, write a letter to someone. Be sure to include all 5 parts of a letter and use commas in the correct places.

An **animal adaptation** is a behavior or physical trait that improves an animal's chance of survival in its natural environment. Adaptations do not happen immediately; they occur over time.

Directions: Read the examples of animal adaptations listed in the table below. Complete the table with additional examples of animals, their adaptations and how the adaptation helps them to survive.

Animal	Adaptation	How it Helps Survival
Polar bear	Thick layers of fat and dense fur	Protects them from cold Arctic temperatures
Giraffe	Long neck	Allows them to reach leaves in tall trees
Chameleon	Camouflage	Protects them from predators by helping them blend in with the natural environment

1. 14 + 43 =

2. 51 + 18 =

3. 97 + 95 =

4. 73 + 61 =

5. 24 + 29 =

6. 88 + 32 =

1. **82 + 20 =**

2. **68 + 32 =**

3. **36 + 77 =**

4. **10 + 92 =**

5. **45 + 54 =**

6. **69 + 86 =**

 FITNESS PLANET → Let's get some fitness in! Go to page 167 to try some fitness activities.

 FITNESS

Read each sentence below. Then answer the questions that follow.

Sentence #1

Sal swam in the salty ocean water while a school of sunfish scurried beneath him.

1. Is this sentence an example of:
   A. Beat
   B. Rhyme
   C. Alliteration

2. How did you know?

....

....

....

....

....

....

Sentence #2

The cat sat on the mat next to the hat.

1. Is this sentence an example of:
   A. Beat
   B. Rhyme
   C. Alliteration

2. How did you know?

....

....

....

....

....

Directions: Write an example of a rhyme and alliteration on the lines below.

➔ Rhyme:

....

....

....

....

....

....

....

....

Alliteration:

....

....

....

....

....

....

....

....

1. 74 + 32 =

2. 32 + 57 =

3. 90 + 16 =

4. 43 + 68 =

5. 15 + 29 =

6. 86 + 40 =

Directions are important. They help you find places on maps, as well as give directions from one place to another. The four **cardinal directions** are north, east, south and west. The **intermediate directions** are northeast, southeast, southwest and northwest. A **compass** is a tool that tells you which direction is north. It can be useful when you are outdoors.

Today, you will need a map or globe to practice identifying directions and finding places. You can use one that you have at home or look for one on the internet.

Directions: Use the map or globe to answer the following questions.

1. Find your state on the map or globe. Which state is located north of your state?

....

2. Find your state on the map or globe. Which state is located east of your state?

....

3. Find your state on the map or globe. Which state is located south of your state?

....

4. Find your state on the map or globe. Which state is located west of your state?

....

5. Find your city on the map or globe. List a city that can be found northeast of your city.

....

6. Find your city on the map or globe. List a city that can be found southeast of your city.

....

7. Find your city on the map or globe. List a city that can be found southwest of your city.

....

8. Find your city on the map or globe. List a city that can be found northwest of your city.

....

9. When might it be important to use a compass?

....

FITNESS PLANET → Let's get some fitness in! Go to page 167 to try some fitness activities.

Grade 1-2

WEEK 8

Let's learn about:

* contractions
* the oo sound
* life cycles
* measurement/data and more!

Ten more or ten less?

1. What is ten more than 50?

2. What is ten more than 30?

3. What is ten less than 70?

4. What is ten more than 20?

5. What is ten less than 60?

6. What is ten less than 80?

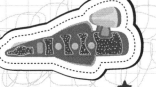

1. What is ten less than 90?

A. 100   C. 80

B. 90   D. 70

2. What is ten more than 40?

A. 30   C. 70

B. 50   D. 90

20 30 **40** 50 60

3. What is ten less than 70?

A. 60   C. 80

B. 70   D. 90

70 − 10 =

4. What is ten less than 50?

A. 20   C. 40

B. 30   D. 60

5. What is ten more than 60?

A. 40   C. 60

B. 50   D. 70

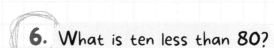

60 + 10 =

6. What is ten less than 80?

A. 60   C. 80

B. 70   D. 90

Contractions are formed by combining two words into one shortened word, using an apostrophe.
An **apostrophe** is a punctuation mark that is used in place of letters in a word.

Examples

Words	Contraction
do not	don't
they are	they're
it is	it's

Directions: Read the words below. Combine the words to form a contraction. Don't forget to use an apostrophe.

1. can not ....

2. he is ....

3. we are ....

4. let us ....

5. they will ....

6. will not ....

7. could not ....

8. she would ....

9. would have ....

10. I am ....

 **FITNESS PLANET** → Let's get some fitness in! Go to page 167 to try some fitness activities.

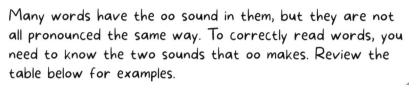

Many words have the oo sound in them, but they are not all pronounced the same way. To correctly read words, you need to know the two sounds that oo makes. Review the table below for examples.

/oo/ as in spoon	/oo/ as in look
boo	book
hoot	foot

Directions: Read the words in the word bank below. Write each word on the correct side of the table below.

Word Bank

spooky	tooth	shook	wood
took	goose	school	hood

/oo/ as in spoon	/oo/ as in look

A **life cycle** is the series of changes that occur during the life of a plant or animal.

Directions: Review the life cycles of the two different animals shown below. Then, answer the questions that follow.

Butterfly

Egg ➡ Caterpillar ➡ Chrysalis ➡ Butterfly

Frog

Egg ➡ Tadpole ➡ Froglet ➡ Frog

Now answer the following questions.

1. How are the life cycles of a frog and butterfly alike?

....

....

....

....

....

....

2. How are the life cycles of a frog and butterfly different?

....

....

....

....

....

....

3. What is another plant or animal that goes through a specific life cycle?

....

....

....

....

....

4. Draw its life cycle below.

Subtracting Multiples of 10

1. 90 - 50 = _____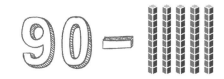

2. 60 - 30 = _____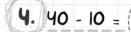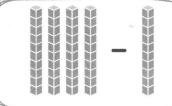

3. 30 - 20 = _____

4. 40 - 10 = _____

5. 50 - 30 = _____

6. 70 - 50 = _____

 **FITNESS PLANET** → Let's get some fitness in! Go to page 167 to try some fitness activities.

Subtracting Multiples of 10

1. 10 - 10 = _____

A. 0   C. 20

B. 10   D. 40

2. 80 - 60 = _____

A. 10   C. 30

B. 20   D. 40

3. 20 - 10 = _____

A. 10   C. 30

B. 20   D. 40

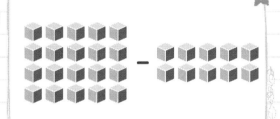

4. 60 - 20 = _____

A. 10   C. 30

B. 20   D. 40

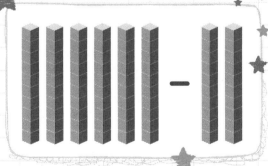

6. 80 - 40 = _____

A. 10   C. 30

B. 20   D. 40

5. 90 - 70 = _____

A. 10   C. 30

B. 20   D. 40

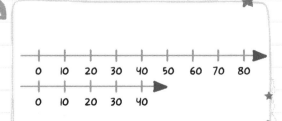

Read the passage below. Then, answer the questions that follow.

Chapter 1 - What is a Narwhal?

A narwhal is a type of whale with a long tusk on its head. Scientists are unsure of the purpose of the tusk which is actually a tooth. Since whales are mammals, narwhals must breathe air to survive. They are able to stay underwater for about 25 minutes before they swim to the surface to breathe.

Chapter 2 - Where Do Narwhals Live?

Narwhals live in the Arctic waters of Canada, Greenland, Norway and Russia. Because they are rare, scientists have not studied narwhals in depth. There is still a lot to learn about these animals.

Chapter 3 - What Do Narwhals Eat?

Narwhals eat squid, shrimp and other fish. They eat more in the winter and store the food for the cold temperatures. Narwhals have many predators, or animals that hunt them for food, including orcas and polar bears.

Chapter 4 - How Do Narwhals Communicate?

Narwhals are social animals. They live in groups of up to 100 whales. They communicate with each other through different sounds and clicks.

Now answer the following questions about the passage.

1. In what chapter would you find information about a narwhal's diet?

   A. Chapter 1
   B. Chapter 2
   C. Chapter 3
   D. Chapter 4

2. What is the tusk on a narwhal's head?

   ....

   ....

   ....

3. What is a predator?

....

....

....

4. Which animals hunt for narwhals?

....

....

....

5. In what chapter might you find information on how narwhals communicate with one another?

    A.   Chapter 1
    B.   Chapter 2
    C.   Chapter 3
    D.   Chapter 4

6. Why is there still a lot to learn about narwhals?

....

....

....

7. How do the chapter numbers and names help the reader?

....

....

....

8. Why is the word "predator" in bold text in the passage?

....

....

....

Tell time in hours and half hours

1. Show 6:30 on the clock.

2. Show 9:00 on the clock.

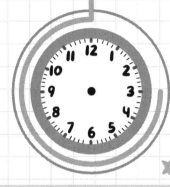

3. Show 4:30 on the clock.

4. Show 2:00 on the clock.

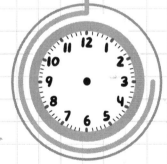

5. Show 7:00 on the clock.

6. Show 8:30 on the clock.

FITNESS PLANET → Let's get some fitness in! Go to page 167 to try some fitness activities.

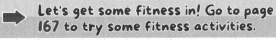

Physical features are things found in a particular area that are naturally made such as landforms or bodies of water.

> Examples: mountains, rivers, peninsulas, oceans, volcanoes and canyons

Human features are things found in a particular area that are man made such as roadways and cultural spots.

> Examples: roads, interstates, libraries, parks, museums

Directions: Using a map of your local community (find one at home or on the internet), identify important physical and human features and answer the questions below.

1. List **3** examples of physical features found in your local community.

A. ....

B. ....

C. ....

2. List **3** examples of human features found in your local community.

A. ....

B. ....

C. ....

3. What is the main difference between a physical feature and a human feature?

....

....

....

....

Grade 1-2
WEEK 9

You'll soon be an expert in:

* comparing length
* possessive nouns
* classifying living organisms
* narrative writing and more!

BRAIN HUNTER

Comparing length

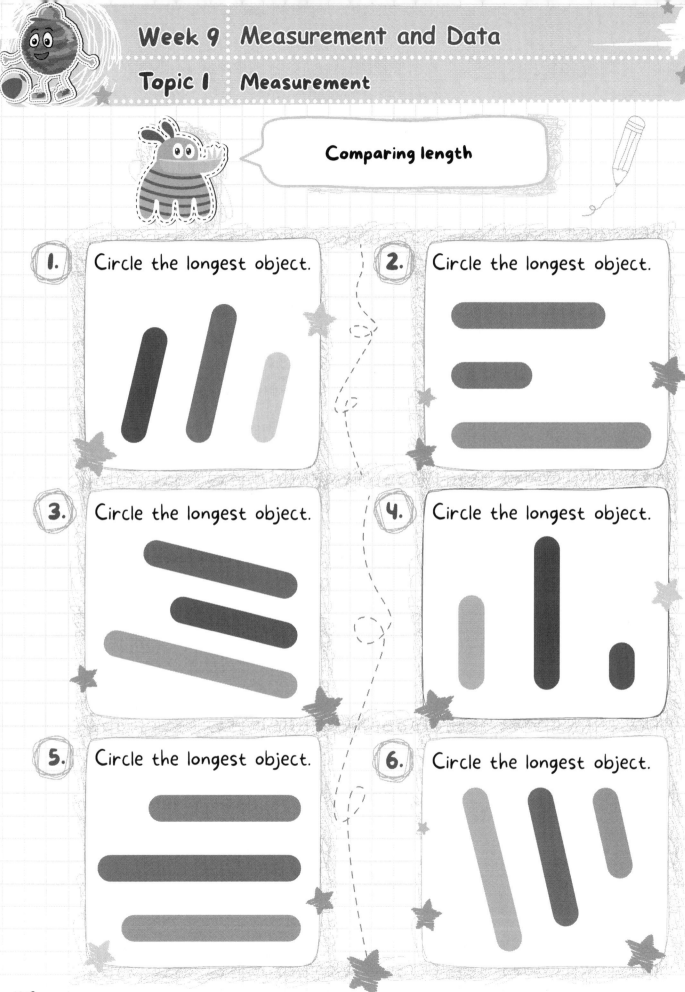

1. Circle the longest object.

2. Circle the longest object.

3. Circle the longest object.

4. Circle the longest object.

5. Circle the longest object.

6. Circle the longest object.

Comparing length

1. Draw a line longer than the object.

2. Draw a line longer than the object.

3. Draw a line shorter than the object.

4. Draw a line shorter than the object.

FITNESS PLANET → Let's get some fitness in! Go to page 167 to try some fitness activities.

FITNESS

A **possessive** is a word that shows ownership. It shows that someone or something owns something else.
When a noun is singular, add an apostrophe and an s to the end of the word to make it a possessive noun.

Examples:

dog bone ➡ dog's bone

girl jacket ➡ girl's jacket

Directions: Read the words below. Add the correct ending to the singular noun to make it possessive.

1. cat tail ➡ ....

2. baby cup ➡ ....

3. dad car ➡ ....

4. teacher pen ➡ ....

5. boy desk ➡ ....

Directions: Read each phrase below. Rewrite it correctly as a possessive. See the example that follows.

the shoe that belongs to the boy ➡ the boy's shoe

1. the popsicle that belongs to my friend ➡ ....

2. the airplane that belongs to the pilot ➡ ....

3. The dog that belongs to my neighbor ➡ ....

Many words have the c sound in them, but they are not all pronounced the same way. To correctly read words, you need to know the two sounds that c makes. Some words have a hard c, as in cat, while others have a soft c, as in cent. Review the table below for examples.

/c/ as in cat	/c/ as in cent
cow	city
can	cell

Directions: Read the words in the word bank below. Write each word on the correct side of the table below.

Word Bank

cap   cup   cereal   cement

cake   circle   cut   cinema

/c/ as in cat	/c/ as in cent

Living things can be classified, or organized, by a variety of physical features, including body covering, number of legs and tail type. These physical features can also help improve an animal's chance to survive in its natural environment.

Directions: Review the examples on the chart below. Complete the chart by filling in the missing physical features for each given animal.

Animal	Body Covering	Number of Legs	Tail Type
Snake	Skin/Scales	0	No Tail
Bird			
Fish			
Frog			
Cheetah			
Giraffe			

Now choose one of the animals from the chart above. Answer the following question.

Animal: ....

How do the physical features of this animal help it to survive?

....

....

....

....

....

FITNESS PLANET ➡ Let's get some fitness in! Go to page 167 to try some fitness activities.

FITNESS

Using a Ruler

1.

How long is the object? _____

2.

How long is the object? _____

3.

How long is the object? _____

4.

How long is the object? _____

5.

How long is the object? _____

6.

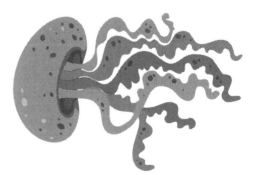

How long is the object? _____

Using a Ruler

1.

How long is the object? _____

2.

How long is the object? _____

3.

How long is the object? _____

4.

How long is the object? _____

5.

How long is the object? _____

6.

How long is the object? _____

Narrative writing is writing to tell a story.

Today you will practice writing a short narrative piece. This organized paragraph will tell a story in a sequential, organized way. You should introduce characters and events, use descriptive words to describe the characters and places in the story, use transition words and provide closure at the end.

You will begin by mapping out your writing and then put it together into a well-organized paragraph with a beginning, middle and end. Think about a story you want to tell. It can be real or imaginary.

Beginning: Establish the situation and introduce your characters.

....
....
....
....

Middle: Develop the story in a sequential manner.

....
....
....
....

Ending: Provide a sense of closure.

....
....
....
....

Now you will use the graphic organizer you created to write a well-organized narrative piece on the lines below. Be sure your writing includes a beginning, middle and end. Remember to write in complete sentences and use capital letters and correct punctuation.

FITNESS PLANET ➡ Let's get some fitness in! Go to page 167 to try some fitness activities.

Analyzing Data

Our class was surveyed about their favorite animal with the following results.

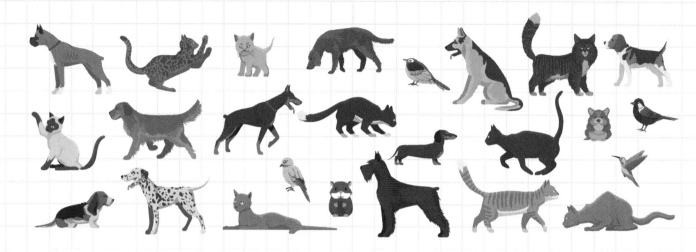

1. What was the most popular pet?

   A. Dogs   C. Birds

   B. Cats   D. Hamsters

2. What was the least popular pet?

   A. Dogs   C. Birds

   B. Cats   D. Hamsters

3. How many total students were surveyed?

   A. 20   C. 25

   B. 23   D. 27

4. How many more students like dogs than cats?

   A. 1   C. 3

   B. 2   D. 4

5. How many fewer students like hamsters than birds?

   A. 1   C. 3

   B. 2   D. 4

6. How many students like cats and birds?

   A. 12   C. 14

   B. 13   D. 15

Demographics are the data that describe a particular place or group.

Today, you are going to explore the demographics of your school community.

Directions: Research and answer the following questions about your school community.

1. How many students attend your school?

....

2. How many grade levels does your school have?

....

3. How many boys attend your school?

....

4. How many girls attend your school?

....

5. How many teachers work at your school?

....

6. How many of the teachers at your school are female?

....

7. How many of the teachers at your school are male?

....

8. How many classrooms does your school have at each grade level?

....

9. How many different cultural or ethnic groups are represented at your school?

....

Grade 1-2
WEEK 10

Let's see what you know about:

* shapes and attributes
* context clues
* irregularly spelled words
* engineering and more!

Looking at Attributes

1. Which shape has **4** sides?

2. Which shapes has **3** sides?

3. Which shape has no corners?

4. Which shape is not a rectangle?

5. Which shape is not a triangle?

6. Which shape is not a square?

FITNESS PLANET → Let's get some fitness in! Go to page 167 to try some fitness activities.

Drawing Shapes

1. Draw a rectangle.

2. Draw 2 rectangles of different sizes.

3. Draw a triangle.

4. Draw a circle.

5. Draw a square.

6. Draw 2 triangles that are different colors.

Context clues are hints that the author gives to help the reader define a difficult or unknown word. Sometimes these hints are found in the same sentence as the unknown word. Sometimes the reader must read the surrounding sentence to figure out the unknown word.

Example - Within the same sentence as the unknown word

The gigantic, or very large, dinosaur fossil was a popular exhibit at the museum.

Example - Within the surrounding sentences of the unknown word

The gigantic dinosaur fossil was a popular exhibit at the museum. The large bones were bigger than a small child!

Directions: Read the sentences below. Choose the best definition from the answer options listed for the underlined word.

1. Her family was very <u>wealthy</u>. They had a lot of money.
   - **A.** rich
   - **B.** poor
   - **C.** lucky
   - **D.** nice

2. Monday was a very <u>bizarre</u>, or strange, day.
   - **A.** fun
   - **B.** normal
   - **C.** strange
   - **D.** bad

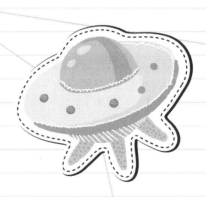

3. Mom's dinner was so <u>delicious</u> that I asked for seconds.
   - **A.** terrible
   - **B.** good
   - **C.** hot
   - **D.** filling

It is common to come across words in books that do not follow common spelling rules. These words are difficult to sound out so it is important to practice reading them until you can read them by sight. Below is a list of common irregularly spelled words.

Directions: Read each word aloud to an adult. Continue practicing any words that you do not know by sight.

the	you	they	are
your	people	whose	should
because	is	know	were
one	again	from	give
of	some	think	once

Directions: Choose 3 words and write each correctly in a sentence.

1. ....

....

....

2. ....

....

....

3. ....

....

....

Last weekend, you were visiting your grandparents in the country and your grandmother told you that small animals kept getting into her garden and munching on the vegetables. She knows that you like to build things so she asked if you could design something to prevent the animals from getting into the garden.

Today you are going to brainstorm different ways to keep the small animals out of the garden. Sketch **3** different ideas below. You will use these sketches in the next few science lessons.

Idea #1

....
....
....
....
....
....
....
....
....
....
....
....

FITNESS PLANET → Let's get some fitness in! Go to page 167 to try some fitness activities.

FITNESS

Idea #2

Idea #3

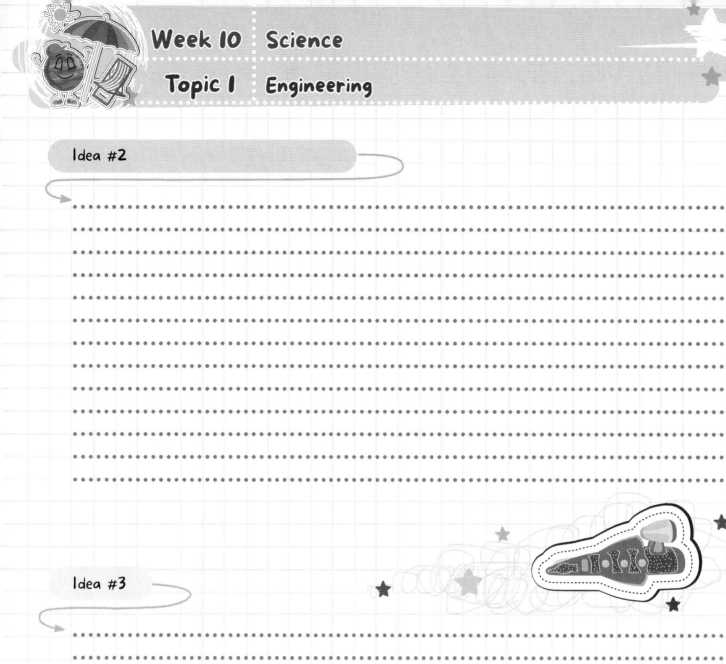

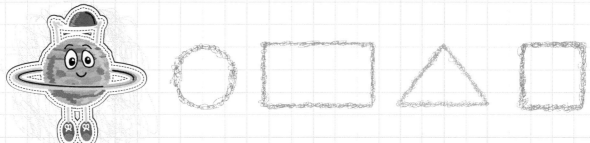

1. Circle the two dimensional shape.

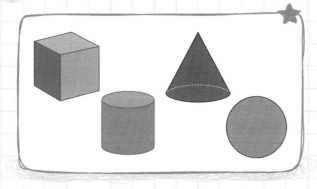

2. Circle the three dimensional shape.

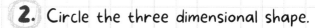
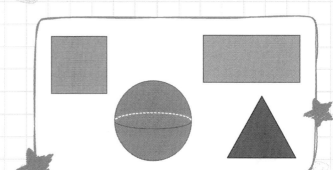

3. Which shape is not a cone?

4. Which shape is not a cube?

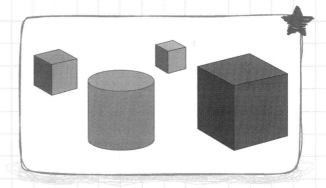

5. Which shape is not a sphere?

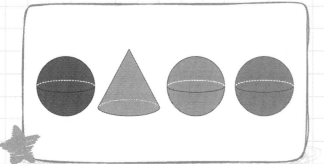

6. Which shape is not a cylinder?

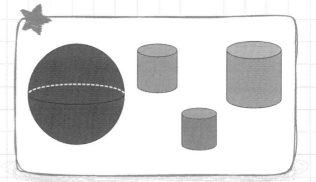

135

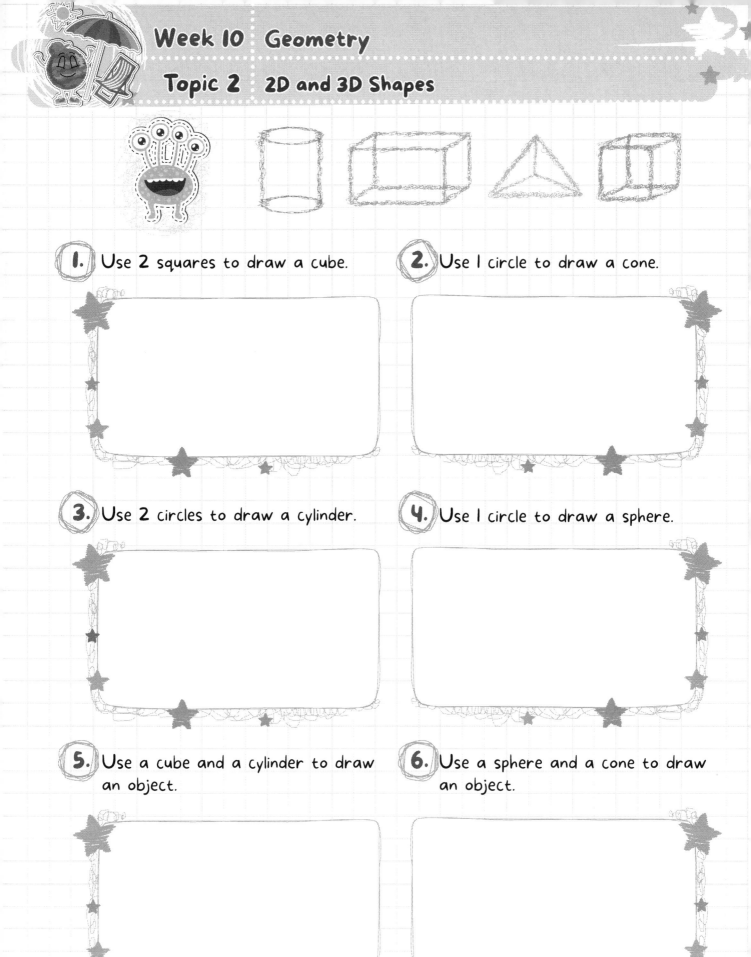

1. Use 2 squares to draw a cube.

2. Use 1 circle to draw a cone.

3. Use 2 circles to draw a cylinder.

4. Use 1 circle to draw a sphere.

5. Use a cube and a cylinder to draw an object.

6. Use a sphere and a cone to draw an object.

Read the passage below to yourself. Then, practice reading it aloud, using different voices for each character in the story. Then, answer the questions below.

Ella woke up early on the day of her birthday party. She was so excited for her friends to come over! She ran downstairs to help her mom put up the decorations.

"Mom! Mom! Is it time to put the decorations up?" Ella shouted.

"Whoa, slow down, Ella. Why don't you have some breakfast first?" Mom suggested.

"OK. Then can we put the decorations up?" Ella pleaded.

"Yes, then we can put the decorations up," Mom replied.

As Ella sat down to eat her waffles, her brothers walked sleepily down the stairs and joined her at the table.

"Mom, can I please go to a friend's house today? The house is going to be full of girls," Ella's brother, Liam, begged.

"Me too! Me too! I don't want to be here with all girls," Ella's other brother, Gray, begged.

"OK boys, I'll see if you can spend some time at the Johnson's today during the party," Mom replied.

Liam and Gray ran up the stairs, cheering, to get ready while mom made the phone call.

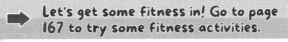

 **FITNESS PLANET** → Let's get some fitness in! Go to page 167 to try some fitness activities.

Once you have practiced reading the passage using different voices for each character in the story, answer the questions below.

1. How many different characters are in the story?

....
....
....

2. What happens at the beginning of the passage?

....
....
....

3. Why don't Ella's brothers want to go to the birthday party?

....
....
....

4. What is mom's solution for Ella's brothers?

....
....
....

5. What happens at the end of the passage?

....
....
....

6. How does Ella feel about her birthday party? How do you know this?

....
....
....

7. Write about a time when you felt really excited for something.

....
....

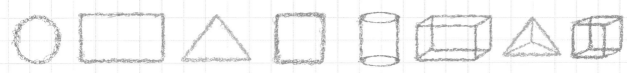

1. Which circle is divided into four equal parts?

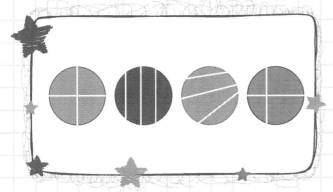

2. Which rectangle is divided into two equal parts?

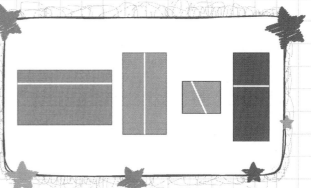

3. How many equal parts are there in this rectangle?

4. How many equal parts are there in this circle.

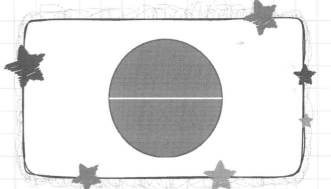

5. Divide the circle into two equal parts and shade one half.

6. Divide the rectangle into four equal parts and shade three fourths.

139

Productive resources are the things used to produce goods and services in a community. There are **3** types of productive resources. They are:

1. Human Resources
2. Natural Resources
3. Capital Resources

Review the table below for examples of each type of productive resource.

Human Resources	Natural Resources	Capital Resources
People	Water	Buildings
	Trees	Tools
	Land	Machines

Directions: Review the table. Then answer the following questions.

1. Why do you think human resources are important to the production of goods and services in a community?

....
....
....
....

2. Why do you think natural resources are important to the production of goods and services in a community?

....
....
....
....

3. Why do you think capital resources are important to the production of goods and services in a community?

....
....
....
....

Grade 1-2
WEEK 11

Get ready to explore:

* operations/algebraic thinking
* compound words
* decoding words
* researching a topic and more!

1. Give **2** facts that belong in the same fact family as 2 + 6 = 8.

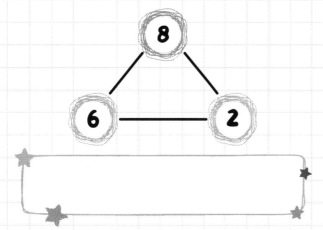

2. Give **2** facts that belong in the same fact family as 1 + 9 = 10.

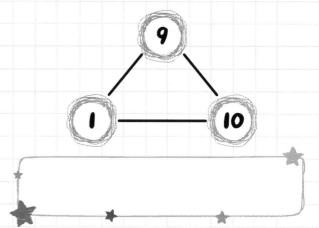

3. Give **2** facts that belong in the same fact family as 3 + 4 = 7.

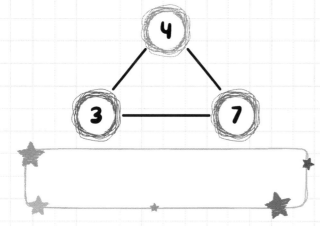

4. Give **2** facts that belong in the same fact family as 12 - 8 = 4.

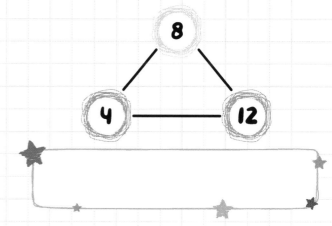

5. Give **2** facts that belong in the same fact family as 7 - 2 = 5.

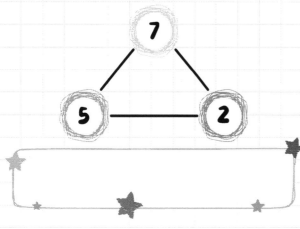

6. Give **2** facts that belong in the same fact family as 16 - 7 = 9.

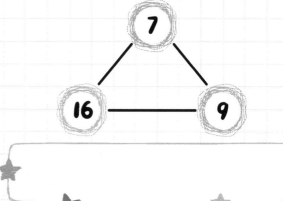

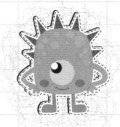

1. ⬭ $+ 1 = 7$

2. $3 + $ ⬭ $= 8$

3. $9 - $ ⬭ $= 4$

4. ⬭ $+ 6 = 10$

5. ⬭ $- 2 = 9$

6. $5 - $ ⬭ $= 3$

FITNESS PLANET → Let's get some fitness in! Go to page 167 to try some fitness activities.

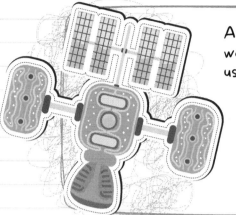

A **compound word** is two words joined together to create one new word. You can often figure out the meaning of a compound word by using the meanings of the two individual words.

Examples:

book + shelf = bookshelf or a shelf for books

sun + light = sunlight or light from the sun

surf + board = surfboard or a board used for surfing

Directions: Figure out the meaning of the compound words below. Write your best guess on the line.

1. moonlight ....

2. toothbrush ....

3. stoplight ....

4. bathtub ....

5. bedroom ....

Directions: Figure out the compound word that matches the meaning given below. Write your answer on the line.

1. A person who fights fires ....

2. A plane that flies in the air ....

3. A machine that washes dishes ....

4. A ring for your ear ....

5. An insect that hops in the grass ....

Week II Phonics Review

Topic 2 Decoding Two Syllable Words with Long Vowels

Good readers must be able to decode, or sound out, words with more than one syllable. These words could include long or short vowels.

Today, you are going to practice reading two syllable words with long vowels. Remember, long vowels say their own name.

Directions: Read aloud the words listed below to someone at home.

became	decide	label
locate	native	even
bonus	notice	divide
alone	table	raincoat
remind	pirate	item
sailboat	eagle	Friday

Directions: Think of 2 two-syllable words that have long vowel sounds. Write them below.

I. ....
....
....

2. ....
....
....

In the last lesson, you sketched different ways to prevent small animals from getting into your grandmother's garden.

Today, you are going to compare and contrast the designs you came up with. Fill out the table below to compare the strengths and weaknesses of each one.

	Strengths	Weaknesses
Design #1		
Design #2		
Design #3		

Follow-Up Questions

1. Which design do you think will work best? Why?

....

....

....

....

....

....

....

....

....

 FITNESS PLANET → Let's get some fitness in! Go to page 167 to try some fitness activities.

1. $1 + 6 =$

2. $8 - 4 =$

3. $3 + 3 =$

4. $5 - 1 =$

5. $12 - 5 =$

6. $5 + 7 =$

1. How can you make 12?

2. What number can you add to 7 to get 11?

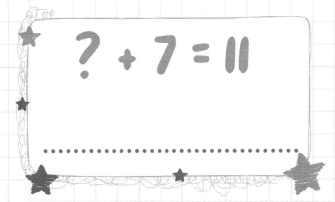

$$? + 7 = 11$$

3. What number can you take away from 13 to get 4?

$$13 - ? = 4$$

4. What number can you add to 4 to get 9?

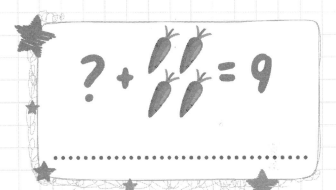

$$? + \text{🥕🥕🥕} = 9$$

5. How can you make 10?

6. What number can you take away from 6 to get 5?

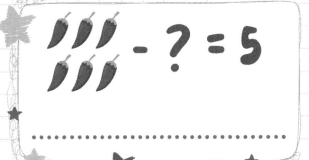

$$\text{🌶️🌶️🌶️🌶️🌶️🌶️} - ? = 5$$

Good writers do a lot of research on the topic they are going to write about. They use different sources to find information. Sources might include books, the internet or interviews with people. This helps them to know a lot about the subject.

Today, you are going to practice this skill by researching a topic that you want to learn more about. Remember, a topic is what you are writing about. It could be a place, an animal, a sport, a person or many other things.

Directions: Choose a topic that you want to learn more about. Find two sources with information on this topic. Study these sources and answer the questions below.

1. Topic: ....

2. Source #1: ....
    ....

3. Write 3 things that you learned about your topic from this source:

    A. ....
    ....

    B. ....
    ....

    C. ....
    ....

4. Source #2: ....
    ....

5. Write 3 things that you learned about your topic from this source:

A. ....

....

B. ....

....

C. ....

....

Directions: Now use the information you learned from doing research to write a well-organized paragraph about your topic. Don't forget to write in complete sentences and use capital letters and punctuation.

....

....

....

....

....

....

....

....

....

....

....

....

....

FITNESS PLANET → Let's get some fitness in! Go to page 167 to try some fitness activities.

FITNESS

1. Circle the longest object.

2. Draw a line longer than the object.

3. Circle the shortest object.

4. How long is the object?

5. If 15 students were surveyed, and 4 students like chocolate ice cream. How many students do not like chocolate ice cream?

$$15 = \text{(ice creams)} + ?$$

6. In a survey, 6 students like vanilla ice cream, 4 students like chocolate and 3 like strawberry. How many students were surveyed in all?

Many communities are known for certain goods that are produced locally or for services that are provided to community members.

Goods are tangible objects such as food, clothes and toys.

Services are actions that someone does for someone else such as trash removal, dry cleaning and car washing.

Today, you are going to research a specific good or service that is produced in your community. Answer the questions below to guide your research.

Good or Service: ....

Who provides this good or service? ....
....

Is this good or service new to your community or has it been available for many years?
....
....
....
....

What productive resources are needed to produce this good or service?
....
....
....
....

Why is this good or service important to your local community?
....
....
....
....

Grade 1-2
WEEK 12

Let's wrap things up with:

* shades of meaning
* engineering
* the g sound
* reading fluency/comprehension and more!

BRAIN HUNTER

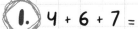

1. 4 + 6 + 7 =

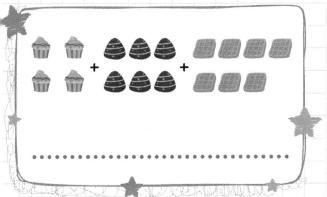

. . . .

2. 2 + 5 + 1 =

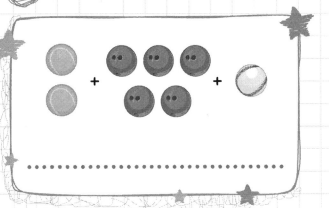

. . . .

3. 6 + 2 + 9 =

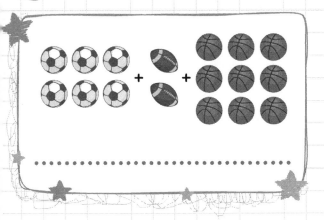

. . . .

4. What number comes next in the sequence? 42 43 44 ____

5. What number completes the sequence? 89 ____ 91 92

6. What number comes first in the sequence? ____ 68 69 70

FITNESS PLANET → Let's get some fitness in! Go to page 167 to try some fitness activities.

FITNESS

1. Draw a set of 9 objects.

2. Draw a set of 16 objects. Circle 10.

3. Draw a set of 21 objects. Circle 10.

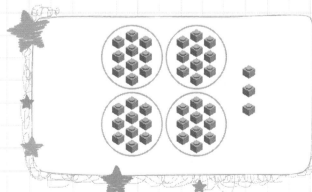

4. How many ones are in this set?

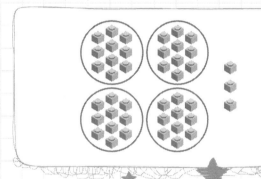

5. Circle the ten groups in this set.

6. How many ten groups are in this set?

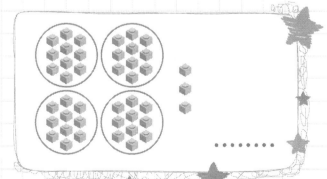

Week 12   Language Review

Topic 1   Shades of Meaning

Shades of meaning refers to the slight differences in meaning between similar words or phrases.

In the example below, see how the meaning of the sentence changes when each word from the chart is inserted into the blank.

The coach asked the player to .... the ball at his teammate.

| toss |
| throw |
| hurl |
| launch |
| fling |

Today, you are going to practice brainstorming verbs (action words) and adjectives (describing words) that are very similar in meaning.

Directions: Fill in the chart below with words that are very similar to the given word. Then write a sentence using each word from the chart, as in the example above.

| big |
| |
| |
| |
| |

Sentence 1: ....

....

Sentence 2: ....

....

Sentence 3: ....
....

Sentence 4: ....
....

Sentence 5: ....
....

yell

Sentence 1: ....
....

Sentence 2: ....
....

Sentence 3: ....
....

Sentence 4: ....
....

Sentence 5: ....
....

In the last two science lessons, you came up with **3** different ideas for keeping small animals out of your grandmother's garden and compared their strengths and weaknesses.

Today, you will choose the BEST idea, sketch it out in detail below and answer some follow-up questions.

Sketch

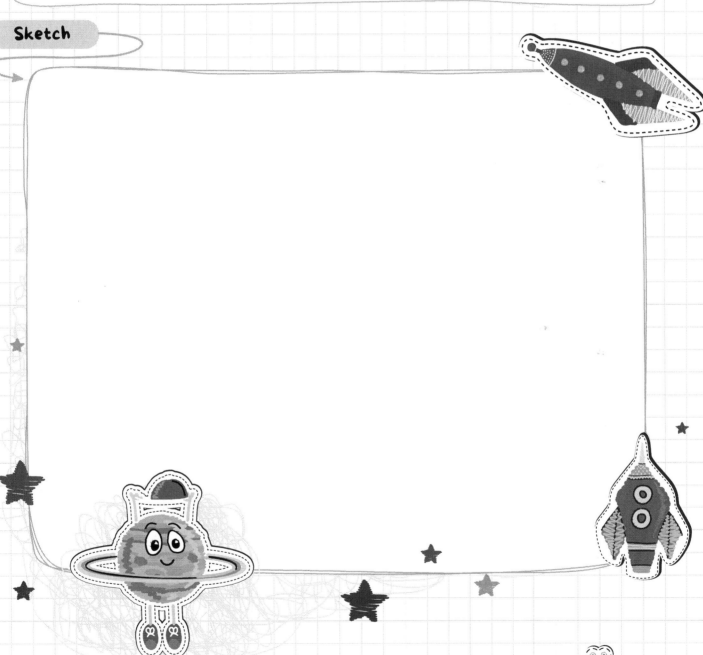

FITNESS PLANET → Let's get some fitness in! Go to page 167 to try some fitness activities.

Follow-Up Questions

1. Write a short summary of how your design works. How will it prevent animals from getting into the garden and eating the vegetables?

....

....

....

....

....

....

....

....

....

....

....

....

....

2. Why did you choose this design from your 3 sketches? What made this design the best for keeping animals out of the garden?

....

....

....

....

....

....

....

....

....

....

....

1. 2 tens + 8 ones=

2. 9 tens + 3 ones =

3. 7 tens=

4. How many tens are in the number 41?

5. How many ones are in the number 60?

6. How many ones are in the number 15?

1. Show the number represented by the words "one hundred twenty - seven."

2. Show the number represented by the words "eighty - one."

3. Show the number represented by the words "forty - five."

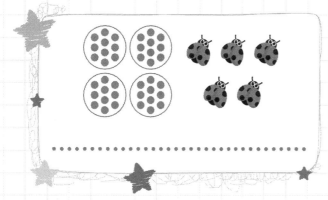

4. Write the word that represents the tens digit value in **72**.

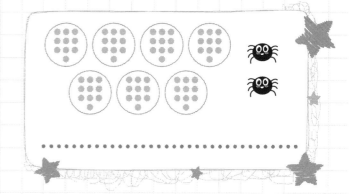

5. Write the word that represents the tens digit value in **69**.

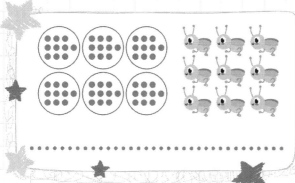

6. Write the word that represents the ones digit value in **21**.

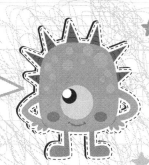

Many words have the g sound in them, but they are not all pronounced the same way. To correctly read words, you need to know the two sounds that g makes. Some words have a hard g, as in goat, while others have a soft g, as in orange. Review the table below for examples.

/g/ as in goat	/g/ as in orange
go	gym
game	gem

Directions: Read the words in the word bank below. Write each word on the correct side of the table below.

Word Bank

giraffe	germ	gas	gum
danger	good	glue	giant

/g/ as in goat	/g/ as in orange

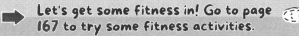

FITNESS PLANET → Let's get some fitness in! Go to page 167 to try some fitness activities.

Directions: Find a book at your house, the library or online that is an appropriate reading level for you. Time yourself reading the book 3 times. After each reading, record how long it took you to read it. Then, follow the directions below.

Book: ....

Reading #1: ....

....

Reading #2: ....

....

Reading #3: ....

....

Now answer the following question.

1. Did you get faster each time you read the book? Why or why not?

....

....

....

....

Directions: Write 3 comprehension questions about the book you read. These could be who, what, why, when, where or how questions.

1. ....

....

2. ....

....

3. ....

....

1. Draw a square.

2. Draw a cube.

3. How many corners are in a triangle?

4. Circle the two dimensional shape: circle, cylinder, cone, or sphere.

5. Divide the circle into equal halves.

6. How many equal parts are in the rectangle?

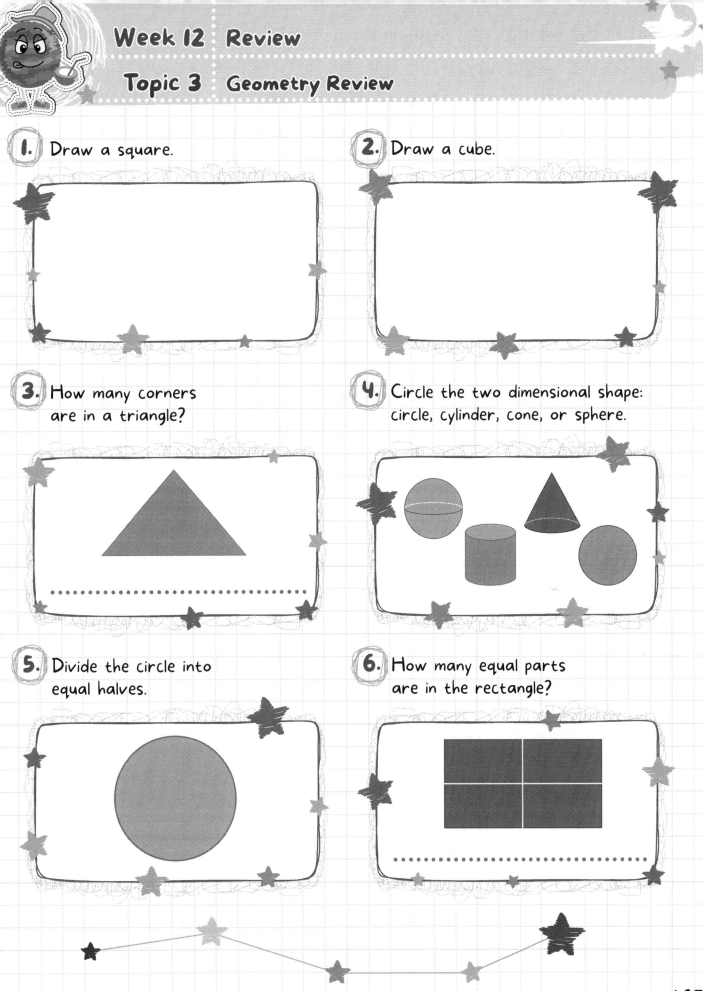

Community workers are people who provide goods and services to the rest of the community.

Examples of community workers include: police officer, firefighter, butcher, doctor and seamstress.

Today, you will research a community worker from your own community. Use this research to answer the following questions.

Community Worker: ....

What good or service does this person provide? ....
....

Which productive resources are necessary for this person's job?

....
....
....
....

How does this person's job benefit the rest of your community?

....
....
....
....

FITNESS PLANET → Let's get some fitness in! Go to page 167 to try some fitness activities.

166

Grade 1-2

FITNESS PLANET

FITNESS PLANET
Repeat these excersises 2 ROUNDS

exercises complex **one**

2 - **Lunges:** 2 times for each leg.
Note: Use your body weight or books as weight to do leg lunges.

1 - **Abs:** 3 times

3 - **Plank:** 6 sec.

4 - **Run:** 50m
Note: Run **25** meters to one side and **25** meters back to the starting position.

Please be aware of your environment and be safe at all times. If you cannot do an exercise, just try your best.

exercises complex **two**

3 - **Waist Hooping:** 10 times.
Note: if you do not have a hoop, pretend you have an imaginary hoop and rotate your hips 10 times.

1 - **High Plank:** 6 sec.

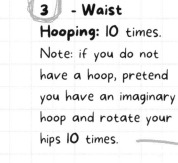

4 - **Abs:** 10 times

2 - **Chair:** 10 sec.
Note: sit on an imaginary chair, keep your back straight.

FITNESS PLANET
Repeat these excersises 2 ROUNDS

exercises complex three

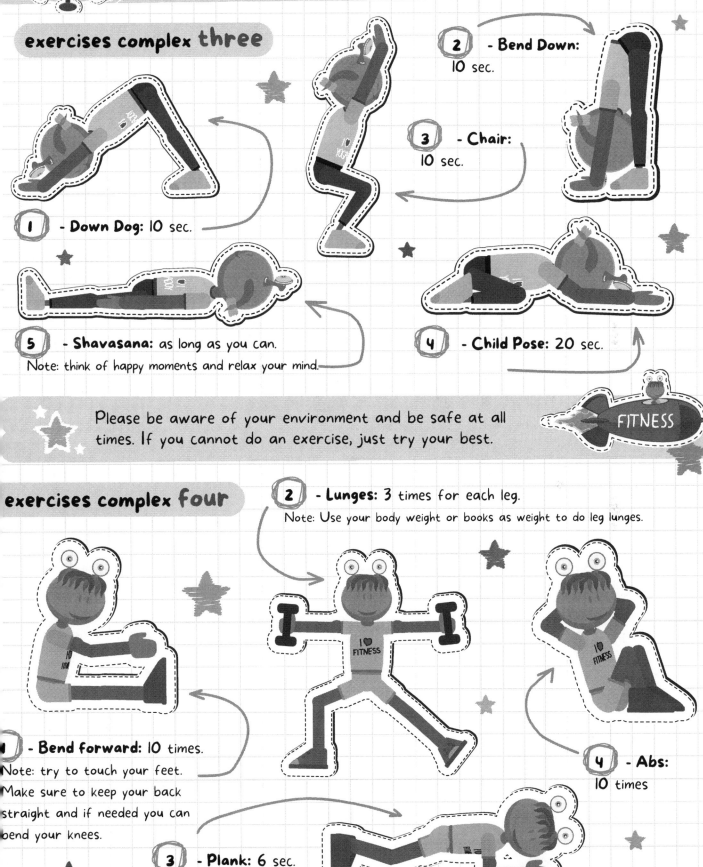

1 - Down Dog: 10 sec.

2 - Bend Down: 10 sec.

3 - Chair: 10 sec.

4 - Child Pose: 20 sec.

5 - Shavasana: as long as you can.
Note: think of happy moments and relax your mind.

Please be aware of your environment and be safe at all times. If you cannot do an exercise, just try your best.

FITNESS

exercises complex four

2 - Lunges: 3 times for each leg.
Note: Use your body weight or books as weight to do leg lunges.

1 - Bend forward: 10 times.
Note: try to touch your feet. Make sure to keep your back straight and if needed you can bend your knees.

3 - Plank: 6 sec.

4 - Abs: 10 times

Grade 1-2

ANSWERS SHEET

ANSWER SHEET

Week 1

★Week 1 ★ Operations and Algebraic Thinking

★ Topic 1 ★ Properties of Operations

★ Page 12 ★	★ Page 13 ★
1. A	1. C
2. A	2. B
3. B	3. A
4. C	4. C
5. B	5. A
6. C	

★ Topic 2 ★ Relating Addition and Subtraction

★ Page 18 ★	★ Page 19 ★
1. 7	1. 6
2. 7	2. 4
3. 5	3. 7
4. 2	4. 2
5. 7	5. 3
6. 5	6. 3

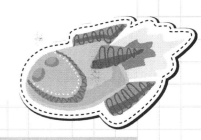

★ Topic 3 ★ Using a Number Line

★ Page 22 ★	
1. 3	4. 6
2. 10	5. 6
3. 7	6. 10

★Week 1 ★ Language Review:

★ Topic 1 ★ Irregular Plural Nouns

★ Page 14 ★	
1. Feet	5. Leaves
2. Fish	6. Children
3. Deer	7. Men
4. Geese	8. People

ANSWER SHEET

★Week 1 ★ Phonics Review

★ Topic 2 ★ Long and Short Vowels

★ Page 15 ★

1. Long vowel
2. Short vowel
3. Short vowel
4. Long vowel
5. Short vowel

Table: answers will vary.

★Week 1 ★ Reading Passage

★ Topic 3 ★ Literature

★ Page 20-21 ★

1. Sam
2. His brother and sister
3. Walking to school, at school
4. Winter; it's cold and snowing
5. He is tired of them complaining about how cold they are.
6. A snowplow drives by and snow flies all over them.
7. She is angry because Sam left them alone and they got covered in snow.
8. Sam feels bad about leaving them alone. He apologizes.
9. Sam's mom is probably going to be angry because he didn't follow the rules.
10. Answers will vary.

★Week 1 ★ Science

★ Topic 1 ★ Classifying Materials

★ Page 16-17 ★

1. All answers will vary.

★Week 1 ★ Social Studies

★ Topic 1 ★ Exploring the History of Your Community

★ Page 23 ★

1. All answers will vary.

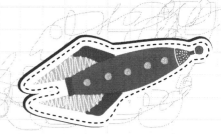

ANSWER SHEET

Week 2

★ Week 2 ★ Operations and Algebraic Thinking

★ Topic 1 ★ Adding and Subtracting to 20

★ Page 25 ★	★ Page 26 ★
1. 6	1. 6
2. 11	2. 2
3. 9	3. 1
4. 11	4. 3
5. 8	5. 0
6. 4	6. 5

★ Topic 2 ★ Adding and Subtracting to 20

★ Page 31 ★	★ Page 32 ★
1. 1	1. 10
2. 10	2. 4
3. 8	3. 11
4. 7	4. 12
5. 7	5. 2
6. 3	6. 3

★ Topic 3 ★ Adding and Subtracting to 20

★ Page 35 ★
1. A
2. B
3. C
4. C
5. C

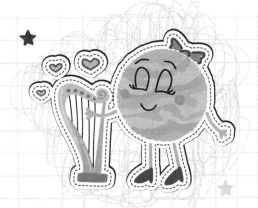

ANSWER SHEET

★Week 2 ★ Language Review

★ Topic 1 ★ Irregular Verbs

★ Page 27 ★

1. I rode my bike to school.
2. My mom paid the cashier at the grocery store.
3. Oliver left the room quietly.
4. I thought about going to the beach.
5. Gabby built a castle with blocks.
6. Sentences will vary.

★Week 2 ★ Phonics Review

★ Topic 2 ★ Vowel Teams

★ Page 28 ★

1. All answers will vary.

★Week 2 ★ Reading Passage

★ Topic 3 ★ Informational Text

★ Page 33-34 ★

1. Red-eared sliders
2. A
3. In the winter
4. The color of their shell darkens.
5. Characteristics of red-eared sliders
6. To become less active during the winter
7. Answers may vary.
8. Answers may vary.

★Week 2 ★ Science

★ Topic 1 ★ Mixing Solids and Liquids

★ Page 29-30 ★

1. All answers will vary.

★Week 2 ★ Social Studies

★ Topic 1 ★ Community Celebrations

★ Page 36 ★

1. All answers will vary.

ANSWER SHEET

Week 3

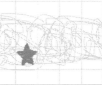

★Week 3 ★ Operations and Algebraic Thinking

★ Topic 1 ★ Addition and Subtract Equations

★ Page 38 ★	★ Page 39 ★
1. B	1. C
2. A	2. B
3. C	3. B
4. B	4. B
5. D	5. C

★ Topic 2 ★ Addition and Subtract Equations

★ Page 44 ★		★ Page 45 ★	
1. 4	4. 4	1. 4	4. 5
2. 2	5. 1	2. 7	5. 4
3. 4	6. 3	3. 1	6. 3

★ Topic 3 ★ Word Problems

★ Page 48 ★	
1. 6 frogs	4. 6 friends
2. 3 frogs	5. 5 umbrellas
3. 7 fish	6. 9 lifeguards

★Week 3 ★ Language Review

★ Topic 1 ★ Verb Tenses

★ Page 40 ★	
Table: 　Shouting, will shout 　Finished, finishing 　Cooked, will cook 　Played, playing 　Climbing, will climb	1. Answers will vary. 2. Answers will vary.

ANSWER SHEET

★Week 3 ★ Phonics Review

★ Topic 2 ★ Prefixes

★ Page 41 ★

1. Preschool
2. Untied
3. Rewrite
4. Before school
5. Not fastened
6. Write again
7. Answers will vary.

★Week 3 ★ Writing Review

★ Topic 3 ★ Opinion Writing

★ Page 46-47 ★

1. All answers will vary.

★Week 3 ★ Science

★ Topic 1 ★ Changes Caused by Heating and Cooling

★ Page 42-43 ★

1. The water changed to ice when cooled.
2. The ice changed back to water when heated.
3. The changes caused to water when heated and cooled can be reversed.
4. A textile such as clothing
5. Once heated, the textile would burn and turn to ash. It is not able to be cooled and returned to its original state.

★Week 3 ★ Social Studies

★ Topic 1 ★ Calendars

★ Page 49 ★

1. All answers will vary.

ANSWER SHEET

Week 4

★ Week 4 ★ Operations and Algebraic Thinking

★ Topic 1 ★ Adding Three Whole Numbers

★ Page 51 ★	★ Page 52 ★
1. B	1. D
2. B	2. C
3. A	3. B
4. C	4. B
5. D	5. C
6. A	6. C

★ Topic 2 ★ Adding Three Whole Numbers

★ Page 57 ★	★ Page 58 ★
1. 16	1. 15
2. 16	2. 22
3. 7	3. 17
4. 16	4. 11
5. 10	5. 15
6. 19	6. 12

★ Topic 3 ★ Word Problems with Three Objects

★ Page 61 ★	
1. 18 stickers	4. 13 books
2. 12 flowers	5. 18 animals
3. 17 bones	6. 7 rooms

★ Week 4 ★ Language Review

★ Topic 1 ★ Adjectives and Adverbs

★ Page 53 ★	★ Page 54 ★
1. All answers may vary.	1. All answers may vary.

ANSWER SHEET

★ Week 4 ★ Reading Passage

★ Topic 2 ★ Literature

★ Page 59-60 ★

1. At the beginning of the passage, the author introduces Grandmother and explains why Tina and her brothers are so excited to see her.
2. Tina and her brothers are excited when Grandmother arrives.
3. Tina was very excited to receive the keychain. She loved it.
4. Answers will vary.
5. She lives in a different state that is far away.
6. Sings, dances, plays games and cooks meals.
7. Tina opens her present, hugs Grandmother and is feeling excited about the rest of her visit.
8. Answers will vary.

★ Week 4 ★ Science

★ Topic 1 ★ Exploring Cloud Types

★ Page 55-56 ★

1. All answers will vary.

★ Week 4 ★ Social Studies

★ Topic 1 ★ Foundations of Government

★ Page 62 ★

Rights: freedom of speech, freedom to own property, right to bear arms, right to vote, equal opportunity rights, freedom of religion

Responsibilities: support and defend the Constitution, vote, stay informed of issues that affect your community, obey laws

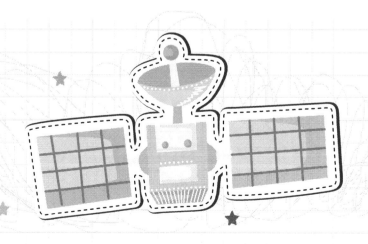

ANSWER SHEET

Week 5

★ Week 5 ★ Numbers and Operations in Base Ten

★ Topic 1 ★ Counting to 120

★ Page 64 ★	★ Page 65 ★
1. 61	1. 39
2. 114	2. 84
3. 26	3. 96
4. 110	4. 15
5. 72	5. 114
6. 48	6. 43

★ Topic 2 ★ Counting objects

★ Page 70 ★	★ Page 71 ★
1. 14	1. Students should circle 15 objects.
2. 29	2. Students should circle 21 objects.
3. 42	3. Students should circle 33 objects.
4. 78	4. Students should circle 64 objects.
5. 37	5. Students should circle 71 objects.
6. 56	6. Students should circle 59 objects.

★ Topic 3 ★ Reading and Writing Numerals

★ Page 74 ★	
1. A	4. C
2. B	5. D
3. D	6. C

★ Week 5 ★ Language Review

★ Topic 1 ★ Simple and Compound Sentences

★ Page 66 ★
1. All answers will vary.

ANSWER SHEET

★Week 5 ★ Phonics Review

★ Topic 2 ★ **Long and Short Vowels**

★ Page 67 ★

1. Short
2. Short
3. Long
4. Short
5. Long
6. Long
7. Short
8. Long
9. Short
10. Long

1. Answers will vary.
2. Answers will vary.
3. Answers will vary.
4. Answers will vary.

★Week 5 ★ Writing Review

★ Topic 3 ★ **Informative/Explanatory Writing**

★ Page 72-73 ★

1. All answers will vary.

★Week 5 ★ Science

★ Topic 1 ★ **Making Weather Observations**

★ Page 68-69 ★

1. All answers will vary.

★Week 5 ★ Social Studies

★ Topic 1 ★ **Community Leaders**

★ Page 75 ★

1. All answers will vary.

ANSWER SHEET

Week 6

★ Week 6 ★ Number and Operations in Base 10

★ Topic 1 ★ Tens and Ones

★ Page 77 ★	★ Page 78 ★
1. Students should circle 10/17 objects.	1. 7
2. Students should circle 10/30 objects.	2. 9
3. 4	3. 5
4. 2	4. 0
5. 8	5. 0
6. 9	6. 4

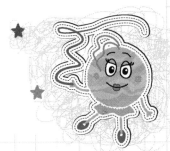

★ Topic 2 ★ Tens and Ones

★ Page 83 ★		★ Page 84 ★	
1. B	4. C	1. B	4. D
2. A	5. A	2. B	5. A
3. C	6. B	3. A	6. D

★ Topic 3 ★ Sets of 10

★ Page 87 ★	
1. 4	4. 1
2. 3	5. 0
3. 6	6. 5

★ Week 6 ★ Language Review

★ Topic 1 ★ Capitalization

★ Page 79 ★	
1. Christmas	1. Answers will vary.
2. Germany, France, England	2. Answers will vary.
3. Mexico, North America, South America	3. Answers will vary.
4. Halloween, July	
5. Tampa, Florida, Atlanta, Georgia	

ANSWER SHEET

★Week 6 ★ Reading Passage

★ Topic 2 ★ Informational Text

★ Page 80 ★

1. B
2. Explain the steps of making a peanut butter and jelly sandwich
3. Gather all ingredients and supplies
4. Press the pieces of bread together
5. How to make a peanut butter and jelly sandwich
6. Answers will vary.

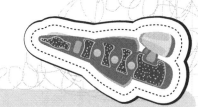

★Week 6 ★ Phonics Review

★ Topic 3 ★ Syllables

★ Page 85 ★	★ Page 86 ★
1. B	1. Answers will vary.
2. C	2. Answers will vary.
3. A	3. Answers will vary.
4. D	4. Answers will vary.
5. B	
6. A	

★Week 6 ★ Science

★ Topic 1 ★ Erosion in Action

★ Page 81-82 ★

1. The wind or water slowly wears away the land, causing it to change shape slowly over time.

★Week 6 ★ Social Studies

★ Topic 1 ★ Traits of Good Citizens

★ Page 88 ★

Character Traits: helpful to others, participates in elections and other community events, volunteers their time to help others, informed of what is happening in the community, actively does things to make the community better

1-2. Answers will vary.

ANSWER SHEET

Week 7

★ Week 7 ★ Numbers and Operations in Base Ten

★ Topic 1 ★ Comparing Two Digit Numbers

★ Page 90 ★	★ Page 91 ★
1. C	1. <
2. B	2. <
3. D	3. >
4. C	4. <
5. A	5. <
6. A	6. >

★ Topic 2 ★ Add within 100

★ Page 96 ★		★ Page 97 ★	
1. 57	4. 134	1. 102	4. 102
2. 69	5. 53	2. 100	5. 99
3. 192	6. 120	3. 113	6. 155

★ Topic 3 ★ Add within 100

★ Page 100 ★	
1. 106	4. 111
2. 89	5. 44
3. 106	6. 126

★ Week 7 ★ Language Review

★ Topic 1 ★ Commas in Letters

★ Page 92 ★	
1. Dear Mr. Jones,	1. A
2. Love, Sue	2. B
3. Thank you, Joe	
4. Dear Mom,	

ANSWER SHEET

★Week 7 ★ Writing Review

★ Topic 2 ★ Friendly Letter

★ Page 93 ★

1. All answers will vary.

★Week 7 ★ Reading Review

★ Topic 3 ★ Poetry

★ Page 98 ★

1. C
2. The sentence has repeating sounds which is alliteration.
3. B
4. Cat, sat, mat and hat all rhyme.

★ Page 99 ★

Rhyme and alliteration answers will vary.

★Week 7 ★ Science

★ Topic 1 ★ Animal Adaptations

★ Page 94-95 ★

1. All answers will vary.

★Week 7 ★ Social Studies

★ Topic 1 ★ Cardinal and Intermediate Directions

★ Page 101 ★

1-8. Answers will vary.
9. Hiking or camping

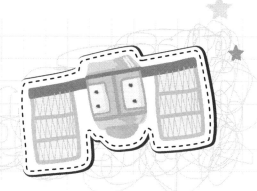

ANSWER SHEET

Week 8

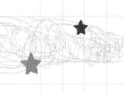

★Week 8 ★ Numbers, Operations and Measurement

★ Topic 1 ★ Numbers and Operations in Base 10

★ Page 103 ★	★ Page 104 ★
1. 60	1. C
2. 40	2. B
3. 60	3. A
4. 30	4. C
5. 50	5. D
6. 70	6. B

★ Topic 2 ★ Numbers and Operations in Base 10

★ Page 109 ★		★ Page 110 ★	
1. 40	4. 30	1. A	4. D
2. 30	5. 20	2. B	5. B
3. 10	6. 20	3. A	6. D

★ Topic 3 ★ Measurement and Data

★ Page 113 ★

1. Students should draw the large hand on the 6 and the small hand on the 6.
2. Students should draw the large hand on the 12 and the small hand on the 9.
3. Students should draw the large hand on the 6 and the small hand on the 4.
4. Students should draw the large hand on the 12 and the small hand on the 2.
5. Students should draw the large hand on the 12 and the small hand on the 7.
6. Students should draw the large hand on the 6 and the small hand on the 8.

★Week 8 ★ Language Review

★ Topic 1 ★ Contractions

★ Page 105 ★

1. Can't
2. He's
3. We're
4. Let's
5. They'll
6. Won't
7. Couldn't
8. She'd
9. Would've
10. I'm

ANSWER SHEET

★Week 8 ★ Phonics Review

★ Topic 2 ★ oo Sound

★ Page 106 ★

/oo/ as in spoon	/oo/ as in look
spooky	shook
goose	wood
tooth	took
school	hood

★Week 8 ★ Reading Passage

★ Topic 3 ★ Informational Text

★ Page 111-112 ★

1. C
2. A tooth
3. A predator is an animal that eats another animal.
4. Orcas and polar bears
5. C
6. Narwhals are rare so scientists haven't studied them in depth.

7. Chapter names and numbers help the reader locate information in the text and know what information is upcoming in the text.
8. The word is in bold because it is a vocabulary word or an important word in the text.

★Week 8 ★ Science

★ Topic 1 ★ Comparing and Contrasting Life Cycles

★ Page 107-108 ★

1. Each has 4 steps, each begins as an egg, each changes from one organism to another during the cycle
2. Frog - last 3 organisms can swim, Butterfly - last 3 organisms cannot all crawl or fly. Frog - changes from baby frog to adult frog, Butterfly - baby butterfly is not part of the life cycle
3. Answers will vary.
4. Answers will vary.

ANSWER SHEET

★Week 8 ★ Social Studies

★ Topic 1 ★ Physical Features of the Local Community

★ Page 114 ★

1-2. Answers will vary.

3. A physical feature is naturally occuring while a human feature is man made.

Week 9

★Week 9 ★ Measurement and Data

★ Topic 1 ★ Measurement

★ Page 116 ★

1. Students should circle the longest line.
2. Students should circle the longest line.
3. Students should circle the longest line.
4. Students should circle the longest line.
5. Students should circle the longest line.
6. Students should circle the longest line.

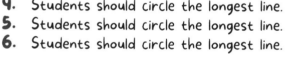

★ Page 117 ★

1. Students should draw a line longer than the given length.
2. Students should draw a line longer than the given length.
3. Students should draw a line longer than the given length.
4. Students should draw a line shorter than the given length.
5. Students should draw a line shorter than the given length.
6. Students should draw a line shorter than the given length.

★ Topic 2 ★ Measuring Objects

★ Page 122 ★

1. 6		4. 3	
2. 2		5. 1	
3. 5		6. 7	

★ Page 123 ★

1. 9		4. 10	
2. 4		5. 2	
3. 5		6. 7	

ANSWER SHEET

★ Topic 3 ★ Analyzing Data

★ Page 126 ★

1.	A	**3.**	C	**5.**	B
2.	D	**4.**	A	**6.**	B

★Week 9 ★ Language Review

★ Topic 1 ★ Possessives

★ Page 118 ★

1. Cat's tail
2. Baby's cup
3. Dad's car
4. Teacher's pen
5. Boy's desk

6. My friend's popsicle
7. The pilot's airplane
8. My neighbor's dog

★Week 9 ★ Phonics Review

★ Topic 2 ★ c Sound

★ Page 119 ★

/c/ as in cat	/c/ as in cent
cap	cereal
cup	cinema
cut	cement
cake	circle

★Week 9 ★ Writing Review

★ Topic 3 ★ Narrative Writing

★ Page 124-125 ★

1. All answers will vary.

ANSWER SHEET

★Week 9 ★ Science

★ Topic 1 ★ Classifying Living Organisms

★ Page 120-121 ★

Table:

Bird	Feathers	2	Small, feathery
Fish	Scales	0	Small, scaly
Frog	Skin/Scales	4	No Tail
Cheetah	Fur	4	Small, furry
Giraffe	Fur	4	Long, furry/ feathery

All other answers will vary.

★Week 9 ★ Social Studies

★ Topic 1 ★ School Demographics

★ Page 127 ★

1. All answers will vary.

Week 10

★Week 10 ★ Geometry

★ Topic 1 ★ 2D Shapes

★ Page 129 ★

1. Students should circle the rectangle.
2. Students should circle the triangle.
3. Students should circle the circle.
4. Students should circle the circle.
5. Students should circle the square.
6. Students should circle the triangle.

★ Page 130 ★

1. Students should draw a rectangle.
2. Students should draw 2 rectangles of different sizes.
3. Students should draw a triangle.
4. Students should draw a circle.
5. Students should draw a square.
6. Students should draw 2 triangles that are different colors.

ANSWER SHEET

★ Topic 2 ★ 2D and 3D Shapes

★ Page 135 ★	★ Page 136 ★

Page 135

1. Students should circle the circle.
2. Students should circle the sphere.
3. Students should circle the cube.
4. Students should circle the cylinder.
5. Students should circle the cone.
6. Students should circle the sphere.

Page 136

1. Students should draw a cube.
2. Students should draw a cone.
3. Students should draw a cylinder.
4. Students should draw a sphere.
5. Students should draw an object with a cube and cylinder.
6. Students should draw an object with a sphere and a cone.

★ Topic 3 ★ Dividing Shapes into Halves and Fourths

★ Page 139 ★

1. Students should circle the blue circle.
2. Students should circle the yellow rectangle.
3. 4
4. 2
5. Students should divide the circle into two equal parts and shade one half.
6. Students should divide the rectangle into four equal parts and shade three fourths.

★Week 10 ★ Language Review

★ Topic 1 ★ Context Clues

★ Page 131 ★

1. A
2. C
3. B

★Week 10 ★ Phonics Review

★ Topic 2 ★ Irregularly Spelled Words

★ Page 132 ★

1. All answers will vary.

ANSWER SHEET

★Week 10 ★ Reading Passage

★ Topic 3 ★ Literature

★ Page 137-138 ★

1. Four
2. Ella wakes up early because she is excited for her birthday party and wants to put the decorations up.
3. They do not want to attend the party because it will be all girls.
4. Mom's solution is to ask a neighbor if the boys can come over during the party.
5. Ella's brothers run upstairs to get ready. They are excited to play with the neighbors.
6. Ella is excited about her birthday party. The reader knows this because Ella is begging mom to put the decorations up.
7. Answers will vary.

★Week 10 ★ Science

★ Topic 1 ★ Engineering

★ Page 133-134 ★

1. All answers will vary.

★Week 10 ★ Social Studies

★ Topic 1 ★ Productive Resources

★ Page 140 ★

1. Humans are needed to do certain jobs to produce goods. They are also needed to provide services to people in the community.
2. Natural resources are needed to create certain goods (paper is made from trees) and provide space for businesses.
3. Capital resources are needed to build certain goods or build buildings for businesses that provide services.

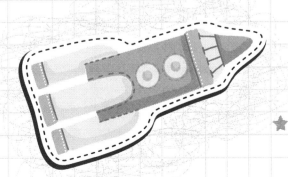

ANSWER SHEET

Week 11

★ Topic 1 ★ Operations and Algebraic Thinking

★ Page 142 ★	★ Page 143 ★
1. Students should present two additional addition or subtraction facts involving the fact family such as 8 - 2 = 6.	**1.** 6
2. Students should present two additional addition or subtraction facts involving the fact family such as 9 + 1 = 10.	**2.** 5
3. Students should present two additional addition or subtraction facts involving the fact family such as 7 - 3 = 4.	**3.** 5
4. Students should present two additional addition or subtraction facts involving the fact family such as 4 + 8 = 12.	**4.** 4
5. Students should present two additional addition or subtraction facts involving the fact family such as 2 + 5 = 7.	**5.** 11
6. Students should present two additional addition or subtraction facts involving the fact family such as 16 - 9 = 7.	**6.** 2

★ Topic 2 ★ Operations and Algebraic Thinking

★ Page 148 ★	★ Page 149 ★
1. 7	**1.** Students should present a way to get 12 through addition or subtraction.
2. 4	**2.** 4
3. 6	**3.** 9
4. 4	**4.** 5
5. 7	**5.** Students should present a way to get 10 through addition or subtraction.
6. 12	**6.** 1

★ Topic 3 ★ Measurement and Data

★ Page 152 ★	
1. Students should circle the longest line.	**4.** 3 cm
2. Students should draw a line longer than 4 inches.	**5.** 11
3. Students should circle the smallest object.	**6.** 13

ANSWER SHEET

★Week 11 ★ Language Review

★ Topic 1 ★ Compound Words

★ Page 144 ★

1. Light from the moon
2. A brush used on teeth
3. A light that tells people to stop
4. A tub used for baths
5. A room with a bed

1. Firefighter
2. Airplane
3. Dishwasher
4. Earring
5. Grasshopper

★Week 11 ★ Phonics Review

★ Topic 2 ★ Decoding Two Syllable Words with Long Vowels

★ Page 145 ★

1. All answers will vary.

★Week 11 ★ Writing Review

★ Topic 3 ★ Researching a Topic

★ Page 150-151 ★

1. All answers will vary.

★Week 11 ★ Science

★ Topic 1 ★ Engineering

★ Page 146-147 ★

1. All answers will vary.

★Week 11 ★ Social Studies

★ Topic 1 ★ Goods and Services in the Local Community

★ Page 153 ★

1. All answers will vary.

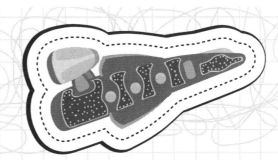

ANSWER SHEET

Week 12

★Week 12 ★ Review

★ Topic 1 ★ Numbers and Base Ten

★ Page 155 ★

1. 17
2. 8
3. 17
4. 45
5. 90
6. 67

★ Page 156 ★

1. Students should draw a set of 9 objects.
2. Students should draw a set of 16 objects. Circle 10.
3. Students should draw a set of 21 objects.
4. 43
5. Students should circle 4 sets.
6. 4

★ Topic 2 ★ Numbers in Base Ten Review

★ Page 161 ★

1. 28
2. 93
3. 70
4. 4
5. 0
6. 5

★ Page 162 ★

1. 127
2. 81
3. 45
4. Seventy or seven
5. Sixty or six
6. One

★ Topic 3 ★ Geometry Review

★ Page 165 ★

1. Students should draw a square.
2. Students should draw a cube.
3. 3
4. Students should circle the circle which is a 2D shape.
5. Students should divide the circle into 2 equal parts.
6. 4

ANSWER SHEET

★Week 12 ★ Language Review

★ Topic 1 ★ Shades of Meaning

★ Page 157 ★	★ Page 158 ★
1. All answers may vary.	1. All answers may vary.

★Week 12 ★ Phonics Review

★ Topic 2 ★ g Sound

★ Page 163 ★

/g/ as in goat	/g/ as in orange
gas	giraffe
gum	germ
good	danger
glue	giant

★Week 12 ★ Reading Passage

★ Topic 3 ★ Reading Fluency and Comprehension

★ Page 164 ★

1. All answers will vary.

★Week 12 ★ Science

★ Topic 1 ★ Engineering

★ Page 159-160 ★

1. All answers will vary.

★Week 12 ★ Social Studies

★ Topic 1 ★ Community Workers

★ Page 166 ★

1. All answers will vary.

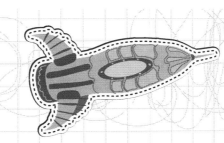

Made in the USA
Middletown, DE
19 June 2020